big NATE

big NATE MAKES THE GRADE

by LINCOLN PEIRCE

SCHOLASTIC INC.

ISBN 978-0-545-52884-9

12 11 10 9 8 7 13 14 15 16 17/0

Printed in the U.S.A. 23

First Scholastic printing, November 2012

A+

SHOPPING FOR BACK-TO-SCHOOL CLOTHES IS USUALLY A TOTAL WASTE OF TIME, BUT **THIS** YEAR I'M ON A **MISSION**!

I'VE **GOT** TO FIND MYSELF A NEW PAIR OF LUCKY SOCKS! MY OLD ONES HAVE JUST ABOUT **HAD** IT!

THEY'VE RUN OUT OF LUCK, EH?
NO, THEY HAVEN'T RUN OUT OF LUCK, FOOL! DO THESE LOOK LIKE THEY'VE RUN OUT OF LUCK?

FROM A SOCK'S PERSPECTIVE, YES.
NOT WASHING 'EM! **THAT'S** WHAT KEEPS 'EM LUCKY!
Peirce

IT'S GONNA BE TOUGH TO FIND NEW SOCKS AS LUCKY AS THESE.
EXCUSE ME, BUT ON WHAT BASIS DO YOU CALL THOSE SOCKS LUCKY?

WHILE WEARING THOSE SOCKS, YOU'VE BEEN PUT ON ACADEMIC PROBATION, RECEIVED 237 DETENTIONS, BEEN REJECTED REPEATEDLY BY JENNY, AND LED THE SOCCER TEAM TO AN 0-AND-14 SEASON!

EXACTLY! THINK WHAT COULD'VE HAPPENED IF I HADN'T BEEN WEARING THESE!

I OBVIOUSLY KNOW NOTHING ABOUT LUCKY SOCKS.
THAT'S WHAT I WAS ABOUT TO SAY, BUT I FIGURED I'D SPARE YOUR FEELINGS.
Peirce

HI, I'M LOOKING FOR SOME SOCKS **EXACTLY** LIKE THESE HERE.

UH... OKAY. ONE PAIR OF GRAY SOCKS, THEN?
GRAY?

THESE ARE **WHITE**!

HOW AM I SUPPOSED TO FIND A NEW PAIR OF LUCKY SOCKS WHEN I'M SURROUNDED BY SUCH INCOMPETENCE?
Peirce

HMM... THESE SOCKS **COULD** BE LUCKY, BUT THERE'S ONLY ONE WAY TO FIND OUT.

EXCUSE ME, MAN. WHERE'S THE CHANGING ROOM?

THE CHANGING ROOM?

KID, YOU CAN'T TRY ON **SOCKS**!
HEY, NOT TO WORRY. THE ATHLETE'S FOOT HAS CLEARED UP COMPLETELY.
PEIRCE

I **THINK** THESE SOCKS MIGHT BE LUCKY, BUT IT'S TOUGH TO BE SURE.
F

I'LL FLIP A COIN! HEADS THEY'RE LUCKY, TAILS THEY'RE NOT!
FLIP!
F

OW! A COIN JUST HIT ME IN THE EYE!
F

I CAN'T SEE!
LET'S HEAD OVER TO THE ARGYLE SECTION.
Peirce
F

SO YOU BOUGHT 'EM, EH?
YUP! THESE HAVE THE POWER! I CAN **FEEL** IT!

I'M GONNA PUT 'EM ON RIGHT AWAY SO THEY CAN START BRINGING ME GOOD LUCK **IMMEDIATELY!!**

HELLO, BOYS

I'D LIKE TO RETURN A PAIR OF SOCKS.
PEIRCE

♪
HEY, EMMITT!

WELL! WHAT ARE YOU GENTS DOING HERE? SCHOOL DOESN'T START 'TIL TUESDAY!
WE KNOW!

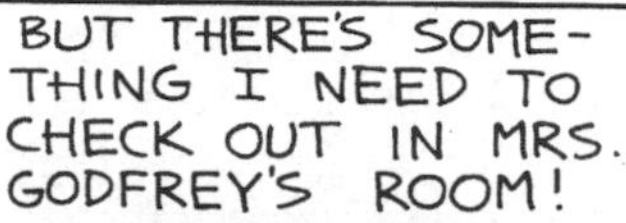
BUT THERE'S SOME-THING I NEED TO CHECK OUT IN MRS. GODFREY'S ROOM!

BE RIGHT BACK!

IT'S STILL THERE!
IT IS?

WA HA HA
A HA HA HA
HA HA HA
HA
HA

I CAN'T BELIEVE IT'S STILL THERE!
HA HA
TOLD YA!
HA HA HA HA HA HA

A CUSTODIAN KNOWS EVERY-THING, AND A CUSTODIAN KNOWS NOTHING.
Peirce

BACK-TO-SCHOOL "DO" and "DON'T" GUIDE!!
by: Nate Wright

DO: Ride the bus!!
PAR-TAY!
Dang! Turn off the 'N Sync!
SCHOOL DISTRICT 3

DON'T: Get driven to school by a parent!
Remember to use those "handi-wipes" after lunch!
I love you, son!

DO: Get back-to-school supplies!
This notebook holds 6 candy bars AND a juice box!
Cool!

DON'T: Get a back-to-school haircut!
What's with the hat?
None o' your beeswax.

DO: Talk to "new kids"!
Well hel-LO there!
Can I show you around?

DON'T: Talk to new teachers!
...And what's your APPROACH to teaching math?
What a BROWN-NOSE!
Let's wedgie him later!

DO: Catch up on all the gossip!
Hey, Dave! How's Sharon?
She... I... We... SOB!
Oh. Sorry, man.

DON'T: Ask Kevin Gladchuk "how was your summer?"
Funny you should ask.
I have here some photos...

DO: Stand up to 7th-grade bullies!

DON'T! DON'T!!
HEY, GUYS! JOIN IN!
TRASH

WELL, THERE IT IS! P.S. 38! MY OWN PERSONAL CHAMBER OF HORRORS! MY MOST HATED ADVERSARY!

BUT I'VE GOT YOUR NUMBER THIS YEAR, YOU HEAR? YOU WILL NOT BREAK ME!! WHAT DO YOU SAY TO THAT?!

YIELD

COULD BE A ROUGH YEAR.
Peirce

HI, MRS. GODFREY!
FRANCIS! WELCOME BACK!

HELLO, MRS. GODFREY!
HI, SHEILA! WELCOME BACK!

WE AGREE ON NOTHING EXCEPT THE FACT THAT IT'S POINTLESS TO PRETEND.
Peirce

I JUST LOVE THE FIRST DAY OF SCHOOL! ALL MY PENCILS ARE SO SHARP! ALL MY PAPER IS SO CLEAN AND CRISP!

AND LOOK AT THIS! DOES ANYTHING SMELL BETTER THAN A BRAND-NEW ERASER?

SSSSNORT!!

AAAAH....
IF YOU THINK THIS IS SCARY, YOU SHOULD HAVE SEEN HIM EARLIER KISSING OUR LOCKER.
peirce

WELL! HELLO, NATE! WELCOME BACK!
HI, MISS CLARKE.

IT **IS** STILL **MISS** CLARKE, ISN'T IT? NO NUPTIAL BLISS OVER VACATION YOU WANT TO MENTION?

NOPE. NO WEDDING RING ON **THAT** FINGER. NO ENGAGEMENT RING EITHER, FOR THAT MATTER.

DULL SUMMER, EH?
FIND A SEAT, NATE.
Peirce

MR. ROSA, I'M READY TO HAVE A **GREAT** YEAR IN ART CLASS! YOU ARE LOOKING AT AN **ART TSUNAMI**!

MY CREATIVE JUICES ARE BUBBLING LIKE **MOLTEN LAVA!** I'M AN ARTISTIC BREAK-THROUGH WAITING TO HAPPEN!

READY THE DISPLAY CASE IN CORRIDOR THREE! I'LL HAVE IT FILLED WITH MASTERPIECES BEFORE YOU CAN SAY "PICASSO"!

SUDDENLY I'M THINKING TOMORROW'S "SOCK PUPPET" ASSIGNMENT MIGHT BE A HARD SELL.
Peirce

I'LL BET MRS. GODFREY READS ME THE RIOT ACT ABOUT NOT GETTING INTO TROUBLE THIS YEAR.
SO TALK TO HER **FIRST**!

TELL HER YOU'RE GOING TO BE A MODEL STUDENT THIS YEAR! FIRE A PRE-EMPTIVE STRIKE!
A PRE-EMPTIVE STRIKE?

A PRE-EMPTIVE STRIKE!

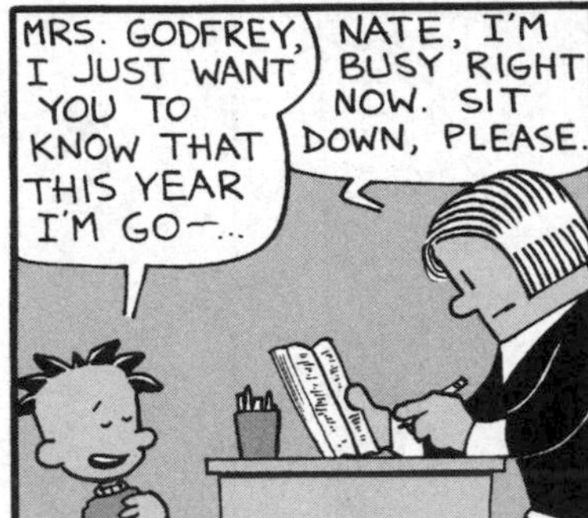
MRS. GODFREY, I JUST WANT YOU TO KNOW THAT THIS YEAR I'M GO—...
NATE, I'M BUSY RIGHT NOW. SIT DOWN, PLEASE.

BUT CAN I JUST TELL YOU THAT I'M...
NATE, DID YOU HEAR WHAT I SAID? SIT **DOWN**, PLEASE!

LOOK, ALL I'M TRYING TO SAY IS...
NATE! I'VE TOLD YOU **TWICE** ALREADY!
NOW, FOR THE THIRD TIME... SIT DOWN!!

THREE PRE-EMPTIVE STRIKES AND YOU'RE OUT.

OH, NO! IT'S GINA!
NICE TO SEE YOU TOO, JERK FACE!

FIND ANOTHER DESK, GINA! I DON'T WANT YOU NEAR ME!
WHY NOT? AFRAID I'LL TRY TO COPY OFF YOU?

HA HA HA HA
HA HA HA HA
HA HA HA

I'VE GOT TO FIND A NEW PEER GROUP.
HA HA
GOOD ONE, GINA!
HA HA
GINA! HIGH FIVE ME!
Peirce

SNIFF! YOUR FEET REEK!
MY FEET? WHAT ABOUT YOUR BREATH, GINA?

YOU CAN SMELL FROM ACROSS THE ROOM WHAT YOU HAD FOR LUNCH! TUNA FISH, NACHO CHEESE DORITOS, BANANA YOGURT, AND ORANGE SODA!

THAT'S WHAT YOU HAD FOR LUNCH.

OH.
HAVE A "CERTS".
PLEASE.
Peirce

GOOD HEAVENS! WHAT'S THAT AWFUL SMELL?
SNIFF SNIFF
MRS. GODFREY

THEY MUST BE BURNING SOMETHING IN THE SCIENCE LAB!
GINA, WILL YOU SHUT THE DOOR, PLEASE?
YES, MRS. GODFREY.
MRS. GODFREY

CHANGE OF PLANS.
HEY, EXCUSE ME FOR HAVING "HOT FEET" SYNDROME!
Peirce

WHAT'S UP WITH YOU AND GINA, NATE?
YEAH! ALL YOU TWO DO IS ARGUE ALL THE TIME!

HEY, YOU WOULD TOO IF SHE SAT NEXT TO YOU! SHE THINKS SHE'S SO GREAT, BUT MAN!... SHE IS JUST TOTALLY OBNOXIOUS!

NATE AND GINA HAVE A "LOVE-HATE" THING GOING ON!
EXACTLY! SHE'S COM-PLETELY...

!... NO!! NOT "LOVE-HATE"!! JUST HATE! IT'S ALL HATE!
OOOOOOOH!
Peirce

HERE COMES MY PET PROJECT!
CHESTER?

CHESTER IS YOUR PET PROJECT?
THAT'S RIGHT! I'M GOING TO REFORM HIM!

REFORM HIM? WHY?
LOOK, EVERYONE'S AFRAID OF THE GUY, RIGHT?

...BUT HE MUST HAVE SOME GOOD IN HIM! NOBODY'S BORN THAT MEAN!

HE ACTS LIKE A BULLY BECAUSE NOBODY'S EVER BEEN NICE TO HIM! IF I TREAT HIM LIKE A FRIEND, HE'LL STOP BEING SUCH A THUG!

IT SAYS SO RIGHT HERE IN THIS BOOK!
PAT PAT

CHESTER, MY MAN!

WHAM!

"UNDERSTANDING BULLIES"
HE'S A WORK IN PROGRESS.
Peirce

NATE, THIS HOMEWORK ASSIGNMENT IS UN-ACCEPTABLE. YOU'LL HAVE TO RE-DO IT.
RE-DO IT?

WE BOTH KNOW YOU'RE CAPABLE OF DOING MUCH BETTER WORK.

IF WE BOTH KNOW IT, WHY SLAP ME WITH EXTRA WORK TO DEMONSTRATE THE OBVIOUS?

SHE NOT ONLY GAVE ME EXTRA WORK, SHE'S MAKING ME JOIN THE FORENSICS TEAM.
F
Peirce

NATE! ARE YOU CHEWING GUM?
MM? MMPH MMM HMMF!

SPIT IT OUT!
HMM MM MMF MMPH HMM!
SPIT IT OUT, NATE! NOW!

SPLUT!

WHAT THE...?
I WAS EATING A "POP TART."
Peirce

I WONDER WHY MRS. GODFREY HATES ME SO MUCH.

THERE'S GOT TO BE **SOME** REASON, BUT FOR THE LIFE OF ME I CAN'T FIGURE OUT WHAT IT IS.

HEY! WHY DON'T WE THINK OF ALL THE THINGS **WE** HATE ABOUT YOU, AND CROSS-REFERENCE THEM WITH STUFF **SHE** MIGHT DESPISE!

GOOD IDEA!

WELL, THERE'S HIS VOICE!
IT'S SO **NASAL!**

SIIIIIIIGH....

SIIIIIIIII

HUCK!... SNORT!...
KOFF KOFF!
KOFF!
KOFF!

I SUCKED UP SOME ERASER DUST ON MY INHALE.
A COMMON CLASS-ROOM HAZARD.
Peirce

HI, MRS. CZERWICKI.
AGAIN, NATE? WHAT DID YOU DO THIS TIME?

NOTHING! IT'S A TOTAL INJUSTICE!
LET ME READ THE NOTE.

ALL I WAS DOING WAS BREATHING! THAT'S IT! SINCE WHEN DO YOU GET DETENTION FOR BREATHING?

WHEN SAID BREATHING FEATURES A "PROLONGED LIP FLAP."
I WAS AIRING OUT MY GUMS!
Peirce

NATE? WHAT ON EARTH ARE YOU GRINNING ABOUT?

NATE!

Z

YESSSS! I GOT A HUNDRED AND FIVE ON THE TEST!
A HUNDRED AND FIVE??

GINA, YOU CAN'T GET HIGHER THAN A HUNDRED!
WELL, I DID! HERE'S WHAT HAPPENED:

DURING THE TEST, I NOTICED THAT MRS. GODFREY HAD MADE A TYPOGRAPHICAL ERROR ON QUESTION SIX!
I CORRECTED HER MIS-TAKE, AND SHE GAVE ME FIVE POINTS EXTRA CREDIT!
HMMM

SO IF I NOTICE A MISTAKE THAT MRS. GODFREY MADE, MAYBE I'LL GET EXTRA CREDIT!
MAYBE! WORKED FOR ME!

MRS. GODFREY?
MMM?

BOY, DID YOU EVER SCREW UP ON QUESTION EIGHT! LET ME SHOW YOU...

FOR YOU, SHE GIVETH. FOR ME, SHE TAKETH AWAY.
Peirce

CLASS ELECTIONS ARE COMING UP.
YUP, AND I'M RUNNING FOR TREASURER!

AGAINST **GINA?**
GOOD **LUCK**, NATE! GINA'S BEEN OUR TREASURER FOR **TWO YEARS!**
I KNOW IT.

SINCE WHEN DO **YOU** WANT TO BE **TREASURER**?
I DON'T, REALLY. I JUST WANT TO BEAT GINA.

SHOULD BE A FUN CAMPAIGN.
I THOUGHT OF RUNNING FOR PRESIDENT AGAINST BRANDON, BUT I HATE GINA JUST A SMIDGE MORE.
Peirce

SIMPLE AND TO THE POINT: "NATE FOR TREASURER"!
EXCEPT YOU DON'T EVEN WANT TO BE TREAS-URER! YOU JUST WANT TO BEAT GINA!
for
ASURE

LOOK, FRANCIS, GINA'S GOOD AT EVERYTHING! SHE'S NEVER COME IN SECOND HER WHOLE LIFE! THAT'S NOT HEALTHY!

AFTER ELECTION DAY, SHE'LL HAVE TO COPE WITH FAILURE FOR A CHANGE! BY BEAT-ING HER, I'LL BE TEACHING HER A VALU-ABLE LIFE LESSON!

THAT'S JUST THE SORT OF WARPED LOGIC YOU LOOK FOR IN A CLASS TREASURER.
PLUS, IT'LL BE FUN!
Peirce

SO IT'S **TRUE**! YOU **ARE** RUNNING AGAINST ME!
THAT'S RIGHT, GINA! MY HAT'S IN THE RING!
NATE

SORRY, NATE, BUT I DON'T THINK YOU'RE THE TREASURER TYPE.
OH, **NO**! THE VOICE OF **AUTHORITY** SAYS I'M NOT THE TREASURER **TYPE**!

WHO ARE YOU TO QUESTION ME, GINA? HOW DO **YOU** KNOW I'M NOT THE TREASURER TYPE? HOW DO YOU KNOW I WOULDN'T MAKE A **GREAT** TREASURER?

WELL, FOR ONE THING, I SIT NEXT TO YOU IN MATH.
SHE'S GOT YOU THERE!
JUST HANG THE POSTERS.
Peirce

SO, MR. CANDIDATE... WHAT'S YOUR PLATFORM?
MY PLATFORM?
NATE for

YES, FOOL! WHAT DO YOU WANT TO DO AS TREASURER?
NOTHING.

I JUST WANT TO KEEP YOU FROM BEING TREASURER.
NATE for TREASURER VOTE!

HE'S THE MAN WHO PUT THE "PETTY" IN PETTY CASH.
CATCHY CAMPAIGN SLOGAN!
Nate
F
Peirce

HI, NATE! CAN I HAVE A STATEMENT FROM YOU FOR THE SCHOOL NEWSPAPER?
WHAT KIND OF STATEMENT?

ALL THE CANDIDATES ARE DOING IT! YOU KNOW, JUST TO LET THE VOTERS KNOW WHAT YOU'LL DO IF ELECTED!

IF ELECTED? THE FIRST THING I'LL DO IS SPEAK TO MY "WORTHY OPPONENT"!

... AND CONGRATULATE HER ON A GOOD CAMPAIGN?
... AND TELL HER "IN YOUR **FACE**, GINA!"
Peirce

SO, WHAT DID MY "WORTHY OPPONENT" SAY WHEN YOU INTERVIEWED HER FOR THE PAPER?
HOW COME YOU KEEP DOING THAT?

DOING WHAT?
THAT THING WITH YOUR FINGERS. YOU DO IT WHEN-EVER YOU SAY "WORTHY OPPONENT."

SO?
SO, IT JUST DOESN'T SEEM ALL THAT... RESPECTFUL.

OOOOH, CRISIS! I'M NOT BEING "RESPECT-FUL"!
SOME ARTICLES WRITE THEM-SELVES.
Peirce

♪

!

NATE FOR TREASURER? IT DOESN'T ADD UP! VOTE FOR GINA!

THE BATTLE IS JOINED.
Peirce

NATE for
TREASURER?
IT DOESN'T
ADD UP!
VOTE
FOR
GINA!

NATE for
TREASURER?
IT!
GINA!

GINA for
TREASURER?
DON'T

HEY!
GAME ON.
GINA for
TREASURER?
DON'T
COUNT
ON IT!
VOTE
NATE!
Peirce

HEY! I'M NATE WRIGHT, CANDIDATE FOR TREASURER! WHO ARE YOU GONNA VOTE FOR?
I'M UNDECIDED.

OH, COME ON! YOU CAN'T SERIOUSLY BE THINKING ABOUT VOTING FOR GINA! I MEAN, GIVE ME A BREAK!

SHE'S SO ANNOYING! SHE'S SO STUCK-UP! IS THAT WHAT YOU WANT? THINK! THE CHOICE BETWEEN HER AND ME IS A NO-BRAINER!

OK, I'M NOT UNDECIDED ANYMORE.
THERE, WAS THAT SO HARD?
Peirce

HOW GOES THE ELECTION?
THAT'S WHAT I'M TRYING TO FIND OUT!

CHESTER! MY MAN! ALL DONE VOTING? WHO'D YOU VOTE FOR?

GET OUTTA MY FACE, YOU LITTLE DORKAZOID.
VOTE

IS THAT WHAT IS CALLED AN "EXIT POLL"?
I'M BEGINNING TO SEE THE BENEFITS OF A MONARCHY.
Peirce

OK, EVERYONE, THE VOTES HAVE BEEN TALLIED AND THE ELECTION RESULTS ARE IN!

BRANDON IS PRESIDENT, SHEILA IS VICE PRESI-DENT, ELIZABETH IS SECRETARY... AND GINA IS TREASURER.
DANG!

IT WAS **CLOSE**, THOUGH, RIGHT? IT **HAD** TO BE CLOSE!
OH, YES. **VERY** CLOSE.

VERY CLOSE TO UNANIMOUS.
SEE, GINA? YOU **LUCKED OUT**!

WELL, YOU WON, GINA! GO AHEAD AND GLOAT! RUB MY NOSE IN IT!
HM? OH, NO, NATE! THAT'S NOT WHAT TODAY IS ALL ABOUT!

THIS ISN'T A VICTORY FOR **ME**! IT'S A TRIUMPH FOR THE VOTERS WHOSE VOICES WERE **HEARD!** THE **REAL** WINNER IS THE **ELECTORAL PROCESS!**

SHE GLOATS GOOD.
Peirce

Hey, TRIVIA BUFFS!
Test your Knowledge!
TAKE the...
Mrs. GODFREY
TRUE or FALSE
QUIZ!

TRUE or FALSE:
In her high school yearbook, Mrs. Godfrey listed her "hobbies" as "unprovoked rage" and "lunch."
What are YOU lookin' at? HUH?

TRUE or FALSE:
At their wedding, Mrs. Godfrey insisted her husband promise to "love, honor, and cower in fear."
whatever you say, dear!

TRUE or FALSE:
In "The Two Towers", Mrs. Godfrey makes a cameo appearance as "Orc #3."
AAARRGHHH
Gandalf! HELP!

TRUE or FALSE:
Mrs. Godfrey's breath has been classified as a "weapon of mass destruction."
tuna
meat loaf
cheese
cabbage
mold
rotten eggs

TRUE or FALSE:
To pay for college, Mrs. Godfrey worked part-time as a Slim-Fast "before" model.

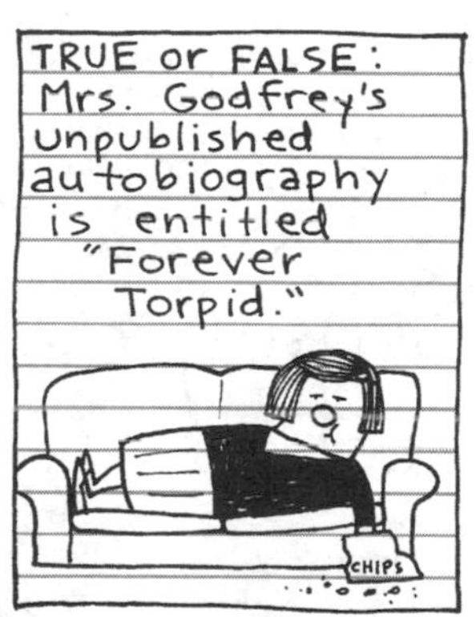

TRUE or FALSE:
Mrs. Godfrey's unpublished autobiography is entitled "Forever Torpid."
CHIPS

CHECK IT OUT! TRUE OR FALSE?

!
!

TRUE.
SO TRUE.
AGAIN?
DETENTION
Peirce

PREPARE TO BE WOWED, MRS. SHIPULSKI! I'M HERE TO READ THE MORNING ANNOUNCEMENTS!
"WOWED"?
MRS. SHIPULSKI

THAT'S RIGHT! I'M GOING TO END WITH A JOKE! I'M GONNA LEAVE 'EM LAUGHING!
THAT'S NOT A GOOD IDEA, NATE.

OH, COME ON! EVERY-ONE LOVES TO HAVE THEIR FUNNY BONE TICKLED, MRS. SHIPULSKI! **YOU** OBVIOUSLY LOVE A GOOD CHUCKLE!
ME?

SURE! LOOK AT ALL THOSE **LAUGH** LINES!
THIS KID'S A RIOT.
MRS. SHIPULSKI
Peirce

...AND FINALLY, TODAY'S FIELD HOCKEY GAME AGAINST BAILEY HAS BEEN POSTPONED UNTIL FRIDAY.

THAT CONCLUDES THIS MORNING'S ANNOUNCEMENTS. PRETTY DULL, EH, GANG? MORNING ANNOUNCEMENTS ARE ONE BIG **SNOOZE-FEST** INSTEAD OF BEING WHAT THEY **COULD** BE: AN **EVENT!**

...AND SO, STARTING TODAY, YOURS TRULY WILL ENDEAVOR TO MAKE OUR TIME TOGETHER EACH MORNING JUST A BIT MORE MEMORABLE!
PLYMOUTH

GUY WALKS INTO A BAR WITH A DUCK ON HIS HEAD...
NATE...
Peirce

NATE, I'M AFRAID I CAN'T ALLOW YOU TO TELL JOKES OVER THE INTERCOM DURING MORNING ANNOUNCE-MENTS.
BUT WHY NOT?

BECAUSE IT HAS NOTHING TO DO WITH **SCHOOL**, THAT'S WHY!
AH! GOTCHA!

SO IF I TOLD A JOKE THAT **DID** HAVE SOMETHING TO DO WITH SCHOOL, THAT WOULD BE OK!

HEY, GANG! HOW MANY MATH TEACHERS DOES IT TAKE TO SCREW IN A LIGHT-BULB?
STOP.
Peirce

SO YOU'RE SAYING I **CAN'T** TELL A JOKE DURING MORNING ANNOUNCE-MENTS?
THAT'S WHAT I'M SAYING.

BUT ALL I'M TRYING TO DO IS BRING A FEW **YUKS** TO THE TABLE!
SORRY, NATE. THAT'S THE WAY IT IS.

IF YOU WANT TO BRIGHTEN PEOPLE'S DAY, YOU'LL HAVE TO DO IT BY READING THE OFFICIALLY APPROVED ANNOUNCEMENTS.

HEY, **HEY**, PEOPLES! **HEAD LICE** SCREENING AT 10:00 TO**DAY**!
MRS. SHIPULSKI, WILL YOU FIND ME SOME TYLENOL®?
Peirce

FINALLY, TODAY'S LUNCH WILL BE FISH STICKS, TATER TOTS, FRUIT CUP AND RAISIN COOKIES.
AND NOW FOR A BRIEF EDITORIAL.

WHEN AN INDIVIDUAL WANTS TO INJECT A TINY BIT OF LEVITY INTO THE SCHOOL DAY AND IS **DENIED** THE CHANCE TO DO SO... **THAT**, MY FRIENDS, IS **CENSORSHIP**!

AND CENSORSHIP IS **WRONG!** DOESN'T SCHOOL TEACH US ABOUT FREE SPEECH? SHOULDN'T MORNING ANNOUNCEMENTS BE A TIME FOR OUR VOICES TO BE **HEARD**? I SAY **YES!!**

THAT CONCLUDES THIS BRIEF EDITORIAL.
Peirce

...AND NOW, **DESPITE** THE FACT THAT THE SCHOOL IS TRYING TO **MUZZLE** ME, I WILL TELL THIS MORNING'S "JOKE OF THE DAY!"
KNOCK KNOCK

AH! HEAR THAT, FOLKS? MR. NICHOLS IS FINALLY GETTING INTO THE SPIRIT OF THINGS WITH A **KNOCK KNOCK** JOKE! WHO'S THERE, MR. NICHOLS?
ANGRY PRINCIPAL.

ANGRY PRINCIPAL **WHO**?
ANGRY PRINCIPAL WHO'S ABOUT TO SEND YOU TO DETENTION.

I DON'T GET IT.
Peirce

WHATCHA GOT?
AN OLD YEAR-BOOK!
OVER IN THE REFERENCE STACKS THEY HAVE COPIES OF EVERY YEAR-BOOK IN THE SCHOOL'S HISTORY!
COOL!
THIS ONE'S FROM TWENTY YEARS AGO! IT'S TOTALLY HILARIOUS!
QUIET PLEASE

IS THAT... MR. GALVIN?
HEE HEE! YUP! HE WAS ACTUALLY YOUNG ONCE!

WOW! LOOK AT MRS. BELLAMY!
SNICKER! TWENTY YEARS AND FORTY POUNDS AGO!

HEY! IS MR. ROSA IN THERE?
LET'S SEE...
FLIP FLIP

MMPH! NICE HAIR!
SNORT! NICE DISCO SHIRT!
HA HA HA
HA HEE HEE
HA HA

HELLO, BOYS.

WA HA HA
HA HA HA HA
HA HA HA HA

THIS IS WHY, DURING FREE PERIODS, I TEND TO STAY IN MY CLASSROOM WITH THE DOOR LOCKED.
HA HA
HA HA
HE'S A DISCO INFERNO!
HA
HA
HA

WE HAVE TO WRITE A HAIKU FOR ENGLISH CLASS!
WHAT'S A HAIKU?
JAPANESE POETRY!

IT'S SUPPOSED TO HAVE SEVENTEEN SYLLABLES!
ALLOW ME TO DEMON-STRATE, TEDDY!

"YOU HAVE CHEEZ DOODLES.
ORANGE, DELICIOUS, CRUNCHY.
GIVE ME ONE RIGHT NOW."

THIS MAY BE THE FIRST TIME A HAIKU HAS BEEN USED TO MOOCH JUNK FOOD.
YOU DIDN'T SAY "PLEASE".
THAT'D BE TOO MANY SYLLABLES.
NARF
NARF NARF
Peirce

DID YOU WRITE YOUR HAIKU?
YUP! IT'S ABOUT MRS. GODFREY!

MRS. **GODFREY?** NATE, IT'S SUPPOSED TO BE ABOUT **NATURE!**
IT **IS!**

"FROM BENEATH HER ROCK SHE OOZES, HER DISGUSTING BREATH REEKING OF SPAM."

THAT'S ABOUT **NATURE?**
THE NATURE OF **EVIL!** PLUS, THERE'S A ROCK IN IT!
Peirce

HEE HEE! I WROTE ANOTHER HILARIOUS HAIKU ABOUT MRS. GODFREY!

LISTEN TO THIS! IT'S SEVENTEEN SYLLABLES OF SHEER POETRY!

AHEM!
"SHE IS A MONSTER: A BLOATED OBSCENITY..."

AND SHE'S RIGHT BEHIND YOU.
NO, THAT'S **EIGHTEEN** SYLLABLES! CAN'T YOU **COUNT**?
PEIRCE

SO! YOU WROTE SOME SORT OF POEM ABOUT ME?
WHAT? I... I... N-NO!

IT DOESN'T EVEN MENTION YOUR NAME, SEE? WHAT MAKES YOU THINK IT'S ABOUT YOU?

I COULD BE RE-FERRING TO SOME OTHER "BLOATED OBSCENITY"!

DETENTION
SIGH...
YOU AGAIN?
Peirce

PSST. WHAT ARE YOU IN FOR?
THROWING FOOD IN THE CAFETERIA. WHAT ABOUT YOU?
LONGFELLOW SCHOOL

I WROTE AN INSULTING HAIKU ABOUT MRS. GODFREY.
HA HA HA
HEH HEH

HA HA HA HA HA
HA HA HA HA HA
HA HA HA HA HA
HA HA HA HA HA
HA

HA
HA
GOOD ONE, MAN!
THE DETERRENCE VALUE OF THE DETENTION ROOM MAY BE FADING.
HA HA
HEY! RECITE IT!
HA
HA HA
HA
MRS. CZERWICKI
Peirce

AHEM!

"I'M IN DETENTION:
AN APPALLING INJUSTICE.
I DON'T BELONG HERE."

PROTEST HAIKU.
SIT DOWN AND BE QUIET.
Peirce

UH... LOOK HERE, YOUNG FELLER...
HOWDY, EMMITT!

I'VE GOT TO MOP THIS HALLWAY. YOU'LL HAVE TO THROW AWAY ALL THIS TRASH.
TRASH? THIS ISN'T TRASH!

LOOKS LIKE TRASH.
ONE MAN'S TRASH IS ANOTHER MAN'S TREASURE!
WHATEVER. THROW IT AWAY.
BUT THERE'S A LOT OF GOOD STUFF IN HERE!
LIKE WHAT?
NAME IT! I CAN FIND ANYTHING IN HERE!

ANYTHING, EH?
ANYTHING!

CHUCKLE! CAN YOU FIND A COPY OF ARTHUR "GUITAR BOOGIE" SMITH'S RECORDING OF "WHO SHOT WILLIE"?

RUSTLE
RUSTLE
RUSTLE

78 OR 45?

GAWK!
HE DOUBTED ME!
WHAT'S WITH THE FRISBEES?
Peirce

NATE, WHY DIDN'T YOU HAND IN YOUR HOMEWORK?
YIP!

I... ER... I DIDN'T HAVE TIME TO DO IT BECAUSE... UH... BECAUSE OF A... A FAMILY EMERGENCY!
OH! I SEE...

WELL, DON'T WORRY ABOUT THE HOMEWORK, NATE. I HOPE EVERYTHING WORKS OUT ALL RIGHT.

I'VE JUST DISCOVERED THE HOLY GRAIL OF EXCUSES!

MRS. GODFREY? I WASN'T ABLE TO DO THE HOMEWORK AGAIN LAST NIGHT.

WE'RE STILL HAVING... UM... A FAMILY EMERGENCY.
I UNDER-STAND, NATE.

LET ME KNOW IF THERE'S ANYTHING I CAN DO.

YOU'RE ALREADY DOING IT.
Peirce

I'M SORRY TO HEAR ABOUT YOUR FAMILY EMERGENCY, NATE. WOULD YOU LIKE TO TALK ABOUT IT?
UH... NO, IT... UM... IT'S TOO PAIN-FUL.
MRS. GODFREY

WELL, DON'T KEEP IT ALL BOTTLED UP! THAT WILL JUST MAKE IT HARDER TO HANDLE!

IF YOU DON'T WANT TO TALK TO A TEACH-ER OR COUNSELOR, AT LEAST FIND A **FRIEND** YOU CAN CONFIDE IN!
OKAY...

PSST! I'VE GOT MRS. GODFREY EATING OUT OF MY HAND!

THIS "FAMILY EMERGENCY" EXCUSE IS THE BEST IDEA I'VE EVER HAD! IT WORKS LIKE A **CHARM**!

NOT ONLY DOES IT GET ME OUT OF DOING HOMEWORK, BUT THE PHRASE "FAMILY EMERGENCY" SOUNDS TOO **PERSONAL** FOR MRS. GODFREY TO ASK FOR ANY DETAILS!

BUT THERE **AREN'T** ANY DETAILS, BECAUSE THE WHOLE THING IS **BOGUS**! RIGHT?
EXACTLY! IT'S **GENIUS**!

HOW 'BOUT A HIGH FIVE?
I'M LEANING MORE TOWARD A SIMPLE SLAP IN THE FACE.
PEIRCE

HI, DAD.
HELLO, SON! GUESS WHO JUST CALLED! MRS. GODFREY!!

SHE WAS CONCERNED ABOUT THE "FAMILY EMERGENCY" YOU'VE BEEN REFERRING TO LATELY AS AN EXCUSE FOR NOT DOING YOUR HOMEWORK!!

YOU CAN IMAGINE HOW... *CHUCKLE!*... AWKWARD IT WAS FOR ME TO TELL HER THERE IS NO FAMILY EMERGENCY!...

...YET.
ER... I'LL BE IN MY ROOM.
Peirce

SO MRS. GODFREY FOUND OUT YOUR "FAMILY EMERGENCY" WAS A SHAM, HUH?
DID SHE EVER.

NOT ONLY DID SHE TIP OFF MY DAD, SHE'S MAKING ME DO ALL THE HOMEWORK I MISSED, **PLUS** AN EXTRA BOOK REPORT, **PLUS** DETENTION UNTIL THANKSGIVING!!

NOT TO MENTION THE FACT THAT, HAVING DONE SOMETHING SO DECEITFUL, YOU'VE PROBABLY LOST A LOT OF SELF-RESPECT.
HUH?

FORGET IT.
OH, HOW I HATE HER.
Peirce

WHAT HAPPENED?
MY BACK WENT OUT DURING THIRD PERIOD.

I'M IN AGONY.
I KNOW WHAT'LL HELP! GET ON THE FLOOR!

MY BROTHER-IN-LAW IS A CHIROPRACTOR! I SAW HIM DO THIS ONCE!

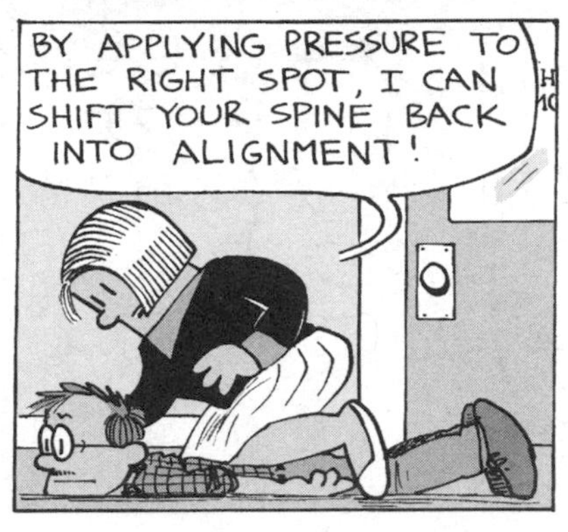
BY APPLYING PRESSURE TO THE RIGHT SPOT, I CAN SHIFT YOUR SPINE BACK INTO ALIGNMENT!

MMPH!
ARRGH!

EVER SEEN THE INSIDE OF THE TEACHERS' LOUNGE?
NOPE.

GIVE YOU A BUCK IF YOU PEEK INSIDE!
YOU'RE ON!

A BUCK DOESN'T COMPENSATE ME FOR THE NIGHTMARES I'LL BE HAVING ALL SUMMER.

SPLOOSH

WHAM!

REMEMBER!!
TODAY IS
SCHOOL
PICTURE
DAY!
Peirce

HEY, YOU'VE GOT A BLACK EYE.
I **KNOW** THAT, FRANCIS! I WALKED INTO A DOOR!

AND YOU'RE ALL MUDDY.
I **KNOW**, I KNOW! A CAR SPLASHED ME!

...AND...
I **KNOW**, FRANCIS! IT'S SCHOOL PICTURE DAY! YOU DON'T HAVE TO POINT THAT OUT! I **KNOW** THAT ALREADY!

GOT A LITTLE ZIT THERE.
I KNOW!
Peirce

NEXT! COME ON IN, KID, AND... WHOA! WHAT HAPPENED TO YOU?
SMILE!
I GOT A BLACK EYE.

THAT'S SOME SHINER! GOT INTO A LITTLE SCUFFLE, DID YOU? A PLAYGROUND RUN-IN WITH THE SCHOOL BULLY?
SMILE!
NOT EXACTLY

HEY, I'VE BEEN THERE, MI AMIGO, I'VE BEEN THERE! YOU WON'T BELIEVE THIS, BUT I USED TO GET TEASED SAVAGELY WHEN I WAS A LAD!

SHOCKER
YOU WEAR A CAPE TO SCHOOL JUST ONCE, AND THERE'S BLOOD IN THE WATER!
Peirce

OKAY, KID, BIG SMILE!
HOLD IT! WHAT ABOUT MY BLACK EYE?

WHAT ABOUT IT?
WELL, CAN'T YOU COVER IT UP? USE SOME SORT OF SPECIAL LIGHT OR LENS OR SOMETHING?

"I'M A DOCTOR, JIM, NOT A MAGICIAN!"
STAR TREK: EPISODE 47, SCENE 32!
HA HA HA
HA HA HA

NOTICE HOW I ESTABLISH RAPPORT BY REFERENCING POP CULTURE.
WHAT A TWIT.
Peirce

HERE, KID... I'LL PUT A LITTLE CONCEALER OVER THAT SHINER.
SMILE!

THIS STUFF IS TICKLY.
NOW WE'LL LET THE MAGIC OF PHOTOGRAPHY DO THE REST!

I... I THINK... I'M GONNA... AH... AHH...
BIG SMILE, KID! SHOW ME SOME TEETH!

MAGIC!
CHOO!
KLIK!
Peirce

NEXT!
HOLD IT, HOLD IT! DON'T I GET A DO-OVER?

SORRY, KID. NO TIME.
BUT I WAS SNEEZING WHEN THE FLASH WENT OFF!

OKAY, OKAY... BUT LET'S MAKE IT SNAPPY!
GOOD!...THANKS! OKAY, HOW DO I LOOK?

IS THERE ANYTHING HANGING OFF MY NOSE?
KLIK!
PEIRCE

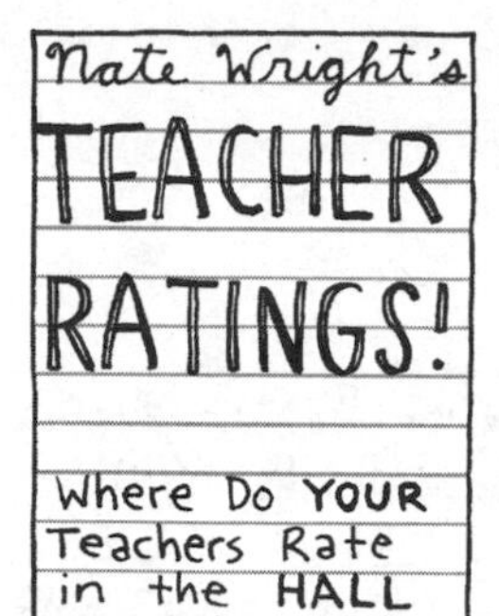
Nate Wright's
TEACHER RATINGS!
Where Do YOUR Teachers Rate in the HALL OF SHAME?

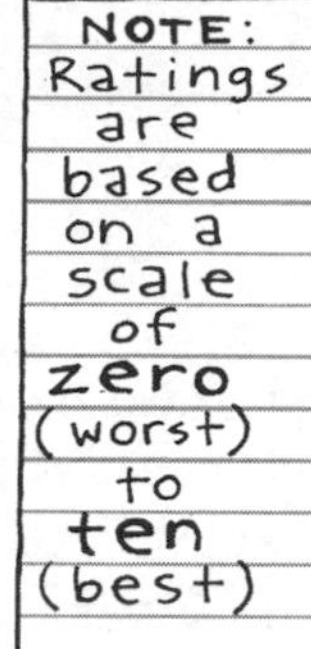
NOTE: Ratings are based on a scale of zero (worst) to ten (best)

MR. STAPLES (Math)
"< fun"
Today, the fascinating world of... FRACTIONS!
RATING: 2.0

MRS. BRINDLE (LIFE SKILLS)
"A recipe for disaster"
... and after 20 minutes, our "johnny-cake" is done!
RATING: 1.3

MS. LA CHANCE (French)
"Ooh La Loser"
Let the words RRRRROLL off your tongue!
RATING: 0.8

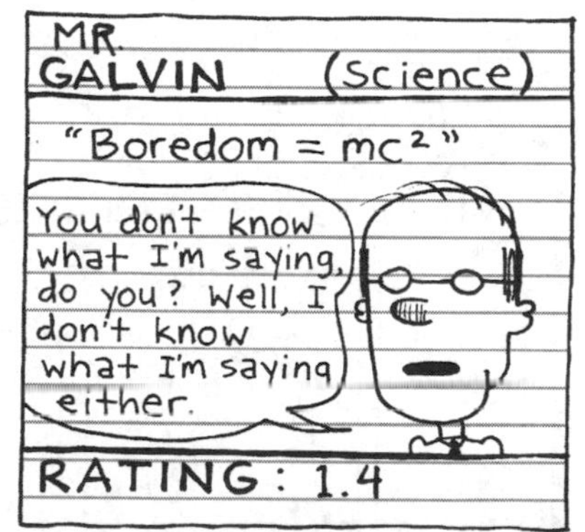
MR. GALVIN (Science)
"Boredom = mc²"
You don't know what I'm saying, do you? Well, I don't know what I'm saying either.
RATING: 1.4

MR. ALDRIDGE (Computer Lab)
Press "escape"
Wait. Wait. That wasn't supposed to... okay, wait. Wait.
tik tak tik tak tik tak
RATING: 1.1

MRS. GODFREY (Social Studies)
"Oh, the humanity."
I summon thee, hounds of Satan!
RATING: −3,000,000

DO YOU ACTUALLY EXPECT ME TO PUT THIS IN THE DISPLAY CASE?
THINK OF IT AS A PUBLIC SERVICE!
Peirce

NATE, WILL YOU RUN THIS NOTE DOWN TO MRS. SHIPULSKI?
SURE, MR. ROSA.

AND... ON YOUR WAY BACK... WILL YOU GRAB ME A CUP OF COFFEE FROM THE TEACHERS' LOUNGE?
THE TEACHERS' LOUNGE?

THERE'S A COFFEE MAKER ON THE TABLE JUST INSIDE THE DOOR.
OK.
MATISSE

"TO BOLDLY GO WHERE NO ONE HAS GONE BEFORE."
Peirce

Teachers' Lounge
KNOK! KNOK!

HMM... NOBODY HERE...

WELL, MR. ROSA SAID TO GO AHEAD AND...

GASP!!
Peirce

WHAT THE...? WHAT IS **THAT** DOING HERE?

THERE AREN'T SUPPOSED TO BE ANY OF THOSE LEFT IN THE SCHOOL! AND YET HERE'S ONE HIDDEN AWAY IN THE **TEACHERS' LOUNGE!**

OH, THE **HYPOCRISY!** THE OUTRIGHT **HYPOCRISY!**

CANDY
Peirce

SO! A CANDY MACHINE IN THE TEACHERS' LOUNGE!
OOP! SOMEONE'S COMING!

CANDY
JINGLE JINGLE

KLINK KLINK
CANDY

AH-HA!
GAH!
Peirce

SUPPOSE YOU EXPLAIN WHY THERE'S A CANDY MACHINE IN THE TEACHERS' LOUNGE!
SUPPOSE **YOU** EX-PLAIN WHY YOU WERE HIDING IN THE RECYCLING BIN!

RECYCLING BIN? YOU MEAN, LIKE, FOR CANS AND...AND...

...BOTTLES...

AH-HA!
SIGH...
SODA

THIS IS AN **OUTRAGE!** THE **TEACHERS** GET **CANDY** WHILE THE **STUDENTS** GET THE **SHAFT**!

REMEMBER LAST YEAR? YOU REPLACED ALL THE CANDY IN **OUR** VENDING MACHINE WITH **HEALTH FOOD**!
AND THAT INITIATIVE WAS A MAJOR SUCCESS!

A MAJOR SUCCESS.

APPARENTLY YOU'VE NEVER SAVORED THE WHOLESOME GOODNESS OF "TOFU TEMPTATIONS."
DARN RIGHT I HAVEN'T.
Peirce

G is for the Gruesome
class she teaches;

O is for Obese, it's
plain to see.

D is for her favorite
Dinner: leeches.

F, the grade she
gives most Frequently.

R is for her Rages
never-ending;

E, her Evil Eye
which never blinks.

Y is for my Youth
which I am spending

sitting in detention.
MAN, THIS STINKS.

MRS. GODFREY, I THINK YOU WENT A LITTLE OVERBOARD ON TO-NIGHT'S HOMEWORK ASSIGNMENT.

I MEAN, FINISHING ALL THESE QUESTIONS IS GOING TO BE IM**POSS**–
MRS. GODFREY?

I FINISHED THE HOMEWORK DURING "FLEX TIME." CAN I HAVE SOME MORE TO DO AT HOME TONIGHT?

CERTAINLY, GINA!
THANKS **SO** MUCH.
Peirce

YOU'RE SUCH A FREAK, GINA! WHO ELSE BUT **YOU** ASKS FOR **EXTRA HOMEWORK**?
I LIKE TO CHALLENGE MYSELF, THAT'S ALL!

UNLIKE **SOME** PEOPLE, I REFUSE TO SETTLE FOR MEDIOCRITY!
WHOA! **WHOA!**

ARE YOU CALLING ME MEDIOCRITISH?

THAT'S NOT QUITE THE WORD I HAD IN MIND.
WELL, I WOULD **HOPE** NOT!
Peirce

MUST YOU KEEP DOING THAT, GINA?
DOING WHAT?

YOU RAISE YOUR HAND EVERY TIME THERE'S A QUESTION TO ANSWER! IT'S LIKE: "LOOK AT ME, PEOPLE! I'M GINA! I'M SMART!"
OH. I SEE.

SO I'M SUPPOSED TO HIDE THE FACT THAT I'M SMART, SO BRAINLESS FOOLS LIKE YOU DON'T LOOK SO BAD IN COMPARISON!
YES! YES!

UH... WAIT. I MEAN...
TAKE YOUR TIME.
Peirce

I DON'T MEASURE MY WORTH BASED ON MY **GRADE POINT AVERAGE**! I'M NOT DEFINED BY MY SCORE ON SOME **MATH TEST**!

HA HA HA
HA HA THAT'S **AWESOME!**
HEH HEH HEH
COOL! HA HA HA
I GOT A 42 ONE TIME!
HA HA HA HA HA

GINA! NATE! I'VE HAD ENOUGH OF YOU TWO **SNIPING** AT EACH OTHER!
YAK YAK YAK YAK YAK

I'M GOING TO SEPARATE YOU.
YOU MEAN... I DON'T HAVE TO SIT IN FRONT OF GINA ANY MORE?

THAT'S CORRECT.
YES!

KOFF! KOFF! KOFF! HACK! ACCK! KOFF!
CAREFUL WHAT YOU WISH FOR.
TISSUES
Peirce

HI, MRS. SHIPULSKI.
HELLO, NATE.

I'M HERE TO SEE PRINCIPAL NICHOLS.
YOU'LL HAVE TO WAIT. ARTUR IS IN WITH HIM RIGHT NOW.

!! ARTUR!!
MM-HM. HAVE A SEAT.
WELL, WELL! WHO WOULD'VE THUNK IT!
ARTUR IS IN THE PRINCIPAL'S OFFICE! I GUESS MR. PERFECT MUST HAVE SCREWED UP!

PRETTY QUIET IN THERE!
CHUCKLE! ARTUR MUST BE SQUIRMING IN HIS SEAT WHILE NICHOLS GIVES HIM THE HAIRY EYEBALL!

WONDERFUL JOB, ARTUR! IT'S BEEN THIRTY YEARS SINCE ONE OF OUR STUDENTS EARNED THE CITYWIDE "GOOD CITIZENSHIP" AWARD!

YOU'VE MADE US VERY PROUD, SON!
WE'LL PUT YOUR PLAQUE IN THE DISPLAY CASE IMMEDIATELY!
THANK YOU, SIR.

NEXT?
OH, HOW I HATE HIM.
Peirce

NATE WRIGHT! ARE YOU PASSING NOTES IN CLASS?

WELL, SUPPOSE I JUST UNFOLD THIS AND READ IT ALOUD FOR EVERYONE TO HEAR!

!? THIS SAYS NOTHING!
THAT'S BECAUSE IT ISN'T A NOTE. IT'S A TABLE FOOTBALL.

AH.
CAN I HAVE THAT BACK? I NEED TO KICK AN EXTRA POINT.
Peirce

HEY, **DWEEB**!
UH OH! IT'S JOSH PANKIN!

YOU'RE IN **TROUBLE**, FRANCIS!
ME? WHAT DID **I** DO?

YOU COVERED UP YOUR PAPER DURING THE TEST SO I COULDN'T COPY OFF YOU! I PROBABLY **FLUNKED** THANKS TO YOU!

THAT'S GONNA COST YOU SOME **COIN**, PINHEAD!
B-BUT I DON'T HAVE ANY MONEY!
HOLD IT, **HOLD** IT!

SETTLE DOWN, JOSH! I'M SURE FRANCIS AND I HAVE SOME CASH IN OUR LOCKER!

RIGHT THIS WAY.

FOOM!

I'LL NEVER CRITICIZE YOU AGAIN FOR BEING A SLOB!
YOU'RE WELCOME!
Peirce

LOOK AT ALL THE **NAMES**! THIS WILL BE THE BIGGEST CHESS TOURNAMENT WE'VE EVER PLAYED IN!
YEAH. AND AS USUAL, MOST OF THE NAMES ARE **BOYS**!
OURNAMENT PAIRINGS

HOW COME SO FEW **GIRLS** PLAY CHESS? THEY CAN BE EVERY BIT AS GOOD AT IT AS **WE** CAN!

I THINK A BIGGER EFFORT SHOULD BE MADE TO GET MORE GIRLS PLAYING IN THESE TOURNAMENTS! WE BOYS OUTNUMBER THEM **TEN TO ONE**!

WOW, I'M SURPRISED TO HEAR SUCH AN ENLIGHTENED...
I MEAN, HOW AM I SUPPOSED TO BAG ANY BABES WITH **THAT** RATIO?
Peirce

IN THE FIRST ROUND, YOU'RE PLAYING SOME-BODY FROM BAILEY MIDDLE SCHOOL... DEREK NACK.
DEREK NACK?
TOURNAMENT

DEREK NACK... HMMM... THAT NAME SOUNDS FAMILIAR... THAT NAME SOUNDS **VERY** FAMILIAR.

I MUST HAVE PLAYED HIM BEFORE, BUT I CAN'T REMEMBER IT. MAYBE WHEN I SEE HIM, IT'LL ALL COME BACK TO...

NATE!!
YIP!
Peirce

NATE! IT'S ME, DEREK! FROM CHESS CAMP LAST SUMMER, REMEMBER?!
YEAH, SURE! HI, DEREK, WHAT'S UP?
NAMENT

WHAT'S UP? WE'RE FIRST ROUND OPPONENTS, THAT'S WHAT'S UP! CAN YOU BELIEVE WE'RE PLAYING EACH OTHER? WHAT A COINCIDENCE!

REMEMBER WHAT A GREAT TIME WE HAD AT CHESS CAMP? REMEMBER WHAT PALS WE WERE? REMEMBER HOW INSEPARABLE WE WERE??

FRIEND OF YOURS?
AS A BARNACLE IS TO A ROCK.
REMEMBER SINGING CHESS SONGS AROUND THE CAMPFIRE?

IS... IS THAT YOUR OPENING?
YUP
I ♥ CHESS

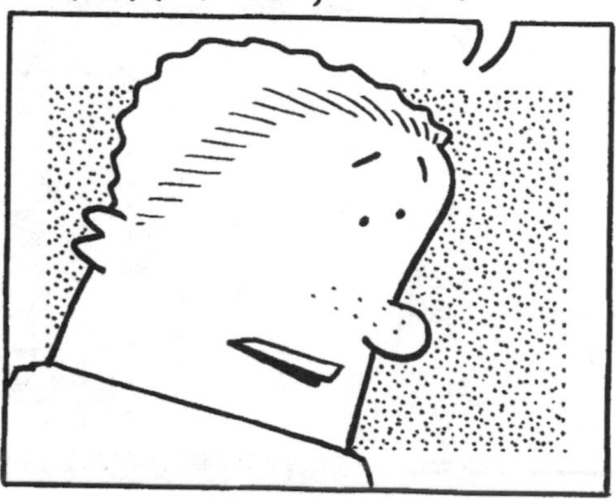
BUT... BUT THAT'S NOT ANY OPENING I'VE EVER SEEN! THAT'S... THAT'S NOT EXACTLY... NORMAL, IS IT?

HMM... HOW CAN I DEFENSE THAT?... WHAT'LL I DO? HMMMM...
I GIVE YOU FIVE MINUTES.

FIVE MINUTES TO MAKE MY MOVE?
NO, THAT'S HOW LONG I THINK THE MATCH WILL LAST.
Peirce

ISN'T THIS JUST LIKE CHESS CAMP, NATE? YOU AND ME, PLAYING CHESS... JUST LIKE LAST SUMMER!
I ♥ CHESS

THINGS HAVE **CHANGED** A BIT SINCE THEN, THOUGH! I'VE BEEN **PRACTICING!** I'M NO LONGER IN **AWE** OF YOU!

OH, YOU TAUGHT ME A FEW THINGS, AND I HAVEN'T FORGOTTEN THEM! IN FACT, YOU JUST MIGHT HAVE TAUGHT ME **TOO WELL**!

MAYBE, JUST **MAYBE**, THE STUDENT HAS SURPASSED THE...
CHECKMATE.
Peirce

WELL, THAT'S THAT. NICE MATCH, DEREK.
YOU BEAT ME, NATE, BUT I DARESAY I EARNED SOME **RESPECT** TODAY!

I WAS THE UNDERDOG, BUT I DIDN'T JUST LIE DOWN AND LET YOU **STEAMROLL** ME! I PLAYED **TOUGH**!

SO LONG, NATE! I BID YOU FAREWELL NOT AS A STARRY-EYED DISCIPLE, BUT AS... AN **EQUAL**!

OH, AND CAN I HAVE YOUR AUTOGRAPH?
Peirce

WELCOME PLAYERS!
TRI-COUNTY SCHOLASTIC CHESS TOURNAMENT
REGISTER HERE

HOW'RE YOU DOING SO FAR?
I WON MY FIRST MATCH!
PAT?

PAT BLEVINS OF AMESBURY MIDDLE SCHOOL VERSUS NATE WRIGHT OF P.S. 38!
HMM... THIS GUY DOESN'T LOOK TOO TOUGH!

STILL, HE'S IN THE WINNER'S BRACKET, SO MAYBE HE'S... HMM? HE'S WHISTLING!

WELL, EITHER HE'S NOT TAKING THE MATCH SERIOUSLY, OR... ?? WHA-?... NOW HE'S EATING CHEEZ DOODLES!
CRUNCH
MUNCH

...AND WHAT SORT OF WEIRD MOVE IS THAT?... DOES THIS KID HAVE ANY IDEA WHAT HE'S DOING?

!! NOW I'VE SEEN EVERYTHING! HE'S READING A COMIC BOOK!
THIS KID'S CLUELESS! I'M GONNA BLOW HIM OFF THE BOARD!

HELLO? IS HE GOING TO DO SOMETHING? DOES HE EVEN KNOW IT'S HIS MOVE?
CHECKMATE
!

HOW'RE YOU DOING SO FAR?
OH, SHUT UP.
Peirce

HAND IN THOSE DRAWINGS, PEOPLE! THEY'RE DUE TODAY!
MR. ROSA? I DON'T HAVE MY DRAWING.

YOU DIDN'T DO IT?
NO, I DID IT! I SPENT **HOURS** ON IT!

WELL, BRING IT IN TOMORROW THEN.
SEE, THAT'S JUST IT! IT'S... IT'S TOO... I **CAN'T** BRING IT IN!

NATE, WHERE IS YOUR DRAWING?
SECOND FLOOR BOYS' BATHROOM, THIRD STALL ON THE LEFT.
Peirce

NATE, WHY ON EARTH DID YOU DO YOUR DRAWING ASSIGNMENT IN A **BATH-ROOM STALL?**
I DIDN'T **SET OUT** TO DO IT THAT WAY!

I JUST HAPPENED TO BE DOODLING ONE DAY, AND IT TURNED INTO THE BEST DRAWING I'VE EVER DONE! SO I KEPT WORKING ON IT!

IT'S RIGHT IN HERE!
HEY!

DO YOU **MIND?**
MOVE IT ALONG, JEFF. WE'VE GOT AN ART CRITIQUE GOING ON HERE.
Peirce

I MUST ADMIT, I'VE NEVER DONE AN ART CRITIQUE IN SUCH A... **UNIQUE** SETTING.
GO ON, MR. ROSA! CHECK OUT MY MASTER-PIECE!

WHAT DO YOU THINK?
HMM... WELL...

COME ON, MR. ROSA! STOP **STALL**ING! GET IT? **STALL**-ING!

CHUCKLE! LITTLE BATH-ROOM HUMOR THERE!
I HAVE A MASTER'S DEGREE.
Peirce

SO!... WHAT DO YOU THINK OF MY DRAWING, MR. ROSA?
WELL, THIS PART ON THE LEFT LOOKS A BIT... OFF.

OFF?
I MEAN, THE PERSPECTIVE DOESN'T LOOK RIGHT.

THAT'S BECAUSE OF HOW YOU'RE **LOOKING** AT IT! YOU'RE AT THE WRONG ANGLE!

YOU NEED TO BE SITTING DOWN!
I'M GETTING A HEADACHE.
Peirce

...AND OVER IN THAT PART, I REALLY TRIED TO MAKE IT LOOK 3-D!
UH-HUH...
AND HOW ABOUT THE WAY I INTEGRATED THE TOILET PAPER DISPENSER INTO THE OVERALL COMPOSITION?
MR. ROSA?
I'M JUST GOING TO GIVE HIM AN "A" AND GET THIS OVER WITH.
Peirce

PRINCIPAL NICHOLS! A CRIME HAS BEEN COMMITTED!
A CRIME?

SOMEONE ERASED THE DRAWING I DID IN THE BOYS' BATHROOM! I WENT IN THERE THIS MORNING AND MY MASTERPIECE WAS GONE!

IT'S AN OUT-RAGE!
HMM... OKAY... LET ME GET THIS STRAIGHT...

YOU DREW ON SCHOOL PROPERTY?
I CREATED "PUBLIC ART."
Peirce

NATE? YOUR HOMEWORK, PLEASE.
I...UH... LEFT IT IN MY LOCKER.

FOOOSHHHHH

I KNOW IT'S IN HERE **SOME**-WHERE.
FIND IT.
OKAY... I'M GOIN' IN.

?

BIFF!

I FOUND...
..... IT.

SHE'S OUT COLD!
I'M GOIN' BACK IN.
Peirce

...AND NOW FOR THE NEXT STEP... I MIX THEM IN WITH WATER!

NOW STEP BACK AND WATCH THE FIRE-WORKS, GANG! THEY SWIM! THEY SQUIRM! THEY DO FLIPS! THEY...

FOR FUTURE REFERENCE, "SEA MONKEYS" ARE NOT A VALID SUBJECT FOR A SCIENCE PROJECT.
I'LL WRITE THAT DOWN.

HI, MRS. CZERWICKI.
AGAIN, NATE?

THIS IS YOUR THIRD DETENTION THIS WEEK!
sigh

!
WOW! IT'S BECKY McGREGOR! I'VE NEVER SEEN HER IN DETENTION BEFORE!

THIS IS MY BIG CHANCE! FOR ONCE SHE'S NOT SURROUNDED BY A PACK OF DROOLING GUYS!

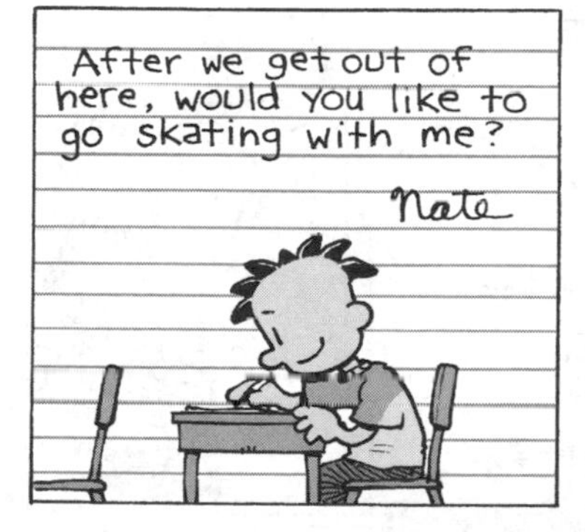
After we get out of here, would you like to go skating with me?
Nate

FOLD FOLD FOLD
ZING!
YIP!

AAARGH! MY GRADE POINT AVERAGE IN SOCIAL STUDIES IS AN 84.2!
SO? THAT'S GOOD!

BUT I NEED TO GET IT TO AN 85! THEN MY DAD WILL LET ME START DOING EXTRA-CURRICULAR ACTIVITIES AGAIN!

MRS. GODFREY GIVES EXTRA CREDIT TO KIDS WHO VOLUNTEER TO BE HER "CLASS-ROOM HELPER."

OH, THE INDIGNITY.
YES?
Peirce

UH... MRS. GODFREY... I WAS WONDERING IF YOU... UM... IF I COULD EARN SOME EXTRA CREDIT BY... UH... BY BEING YOUR... COUGH! CLASSROOM HELPER...

NOT RIGHT NOW, NATE. I ALREADY HAVE A HELPER.
OH... OKAY.

PHEEEEYOO!

ER... I MEAN... 'BYE.
RIGHT

WELL? DID YOU ASK MRS. GODFREY IF YOU COULD BE HER CLASSROOM HELPER?
I DID

SHE TURNED ME DOWN. SHE ALREADY HAS A HELPER.
TOO BAD, NATE. THAT WOULD'VE BEEN AN EASY WAY TO GET EXTRA CREDIT.

I'M KIND OF RELIEVED, ACTUALLY. BECOMING A HELPER FOR MRS. GODFREY MIGHT VERY WELL HAVE TURNED ME INTO.... INTO...

IT'S TOO AWFUL TO THINK ABOUT.
YES, MRS. GODFREY! COLLATED AND STAPLED! RIGHT AWAY, MRS. GODFREY!

SHLOX-TV presents...
SURVIVE... OR ELSE!!
with your host: KEN DOOLITTLE!!

Here we are again, friends, in the Social Studies classroom where our intrepid survivors have been TRAPPED since early September!
Z

They've had to endure countless hardships...
Have we EVER! Lectures, film strips, pop quizzes... Oh, the HORROR!
whimper

...And it's all because of MRS. GODFREY! She's making it IMPOSSIBLE to survive in here!
NATE - 6th grade tribe

Hmm... Sounds like you want to vote Mrs. Godfrey OUT of the classroom!
Oh, I DO!
So do I!
Me too!
And me!

Well, Mrs. Godfrey, the survivors have voted, and it looks like you're —
HOLD it, Ken. I didn't cast MY vote.

But...
No buts! What these "survivors" think is IRRELEVANT! I'm not going ANYWHERE!

I run this classroom, and I decide who stays and who goes!

THANK YOU, GINA. EXCELLENT JOB ON YOUR ORAL REPORT!
THANK YOU, MRS. GODFREY.

YES, GINA, EXCELLENT JOB OF BORING US TO DEATH! THAT REPORT WAS A SIX-HOUR LAYOVER IN YAWN CITY!

NATE? YOU'RE NEXT.
HAVE A SEAT, GINA! WATCH AN ORAL REPORT WITH SOME REAL FLAIR!

NATE!
PREPARE TO BE DAZZLED!
Peirce

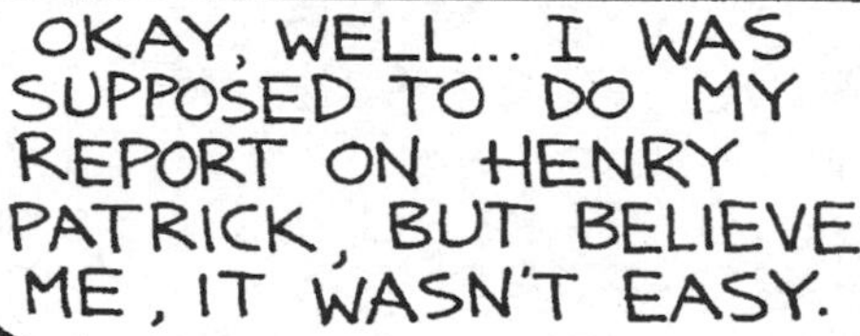
OKAY, WELL... I WAS SUPPOSED TO DO MY REPORT ON HENRY PATRICK, BUT BELIEVE ME, IT WASN'T EASY.

I MEAN, EITHER THIS GUY IS ONE OF THE MOST OBSCURE PEOPLE IN HISTORY, OR...
NATE, YOU WERE **SUPPOSED** TO DO A REPORT ON **PATRICK HENRY**!

HUH?... NO, THE SHEET YOU GAVE ME SAYS HENRY PATRICK!

HENRY, **COMMA**, PATRICK!
THAT'S ANOTHER THING: WHAT KIND OF FREAK HAS A **COMMA** FOR A MIDDLE NAME?
Peirce

HOW COME YOU GOT AN A ON YOUR RE-PORT AND I ONLY GOT A D+?

BECAUSE MINE IS FIVE PAGES LONG, NEATLY WRITTEN, AND CAREFULLY RESEARCHED.

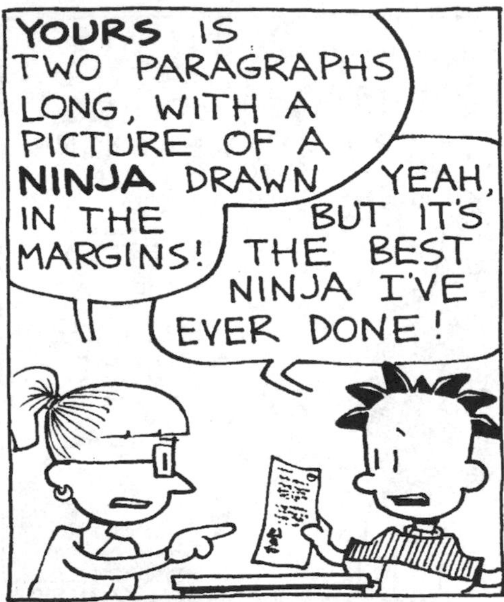
YOURS IS TWO PARAGRAPHS LONG, WITH A PICTURE OF A NINJA DRAWN IN THE MARGINS!
YEAH, BUT IT'S THE BEST NINJA I'VE EVER DONE!

I SHOULD GET SOME CREDIT FOR THE SWORD! CHECK OUT THIS SWORD!
WELL, WHEN YOU PUT IT THAT WAY... HELLO, HONOR ROLL!
Peirce

NYAA!

WHAT? WHAT?
AN EIGHT! I GOT AN EIGHT ON THE SOCIAL STUDIES TEST!

RELAX, RELAX! YOU'RE HOLDING THE PAGE UPSIDE-DOWN. TURN IT OVER.
OH. OKAY. PHEW.

HEY!
Peirce

I'M HERE TO PROTEST, MRS. GODFREY! YESTERDAY'S EXAM WAS **TOTALLY** UNFAIR!
IN WHAT WAY?

IN **EVERY** WAY! LIKE ALL OF YOUR "TESTS," IT WAS CULTURALLY BIASED!

IT **COMPLETELY** DISCRIMINATED AGAINST PEOPLE WHO COULDN'T CARE LESS ABOUT SOCIAL STUDIES!

HENRY FORD! **GERALD** FORD! WHAT'S THE **DIFF?**
YES, NATE. THAT WAS INTENTION-AL.

IT'S ASTONISHING THAT ANY BROTHER OF ELLEN WRIGHT'S WOULD HAND IN SUCH SLOPPY HOMEWORK.

COMPARING ME TO MY OLDER SISTER! MAN, DO I HATE THAT! IT'S SO **UNFAIR**!

I'M NOT HER, I'M **ME**! I'M MY OWN PERSON! I'VE GOT MY OWN SKILLS! MY OWN TALENTS! MY OWN UNIQUE ABILITIES!
F

SUCH AS YOUR UNCANNY IMPRESSION OF MRS. CZERWICKI EATING A "TATER TOT"?
... BUT DO I GET A **GRADE** FOR THAT? **NO**!

TED-DY!
OH, NO.

HI, CINDY.
ARE YOU WALKING HOME? 'CAUSE **I'M** WALKING HOME! WANNA WALK TOGETHER?

UH... WELL, I...
WE COULD GO TO **MY** HOUSE! WANNA GO TO MY HOUSE? WE COULD DO THE MATH HOMEWORK TOGETHER!

KOFF! I... UM... I DON'T...
... BECAUSE YOU'RE SO **GOOD** AT MATH! AND YOU EXPLAIN THINGS SO WELL!

'SCUSE ME.

KLIK!
FOOOOOMM

I SAW YOU WERE IN TROUBLE!
MY HERO!
Peirce

NATE WRIGHT, YEARBOOK PHOTOGRAPHER, AT YOUR SERVICE, MR. ROSA! I'LL BE LOOKING TO GET A GOOD CANDID PHOTO OF YOU LATER TODAY.

CANDIDS ARE SUPPOSED TO BE A **SURPRISE**, AREN'T THEY? IF YOU'RE GOING TO TAKE A CANDID PHOTO, WHY TELL ME BEFOREHAND?

I JUST THOUGHT YOU MIGHT APPRECIATE A LITTLE ADVANCE WARNING.

YOU KNOW... AFTER LAST YEAR'S UNFORTUNATE NOSE-PICKING INCIDENT.
I WAS GROOMING MY MUSTACHE.

POOF!

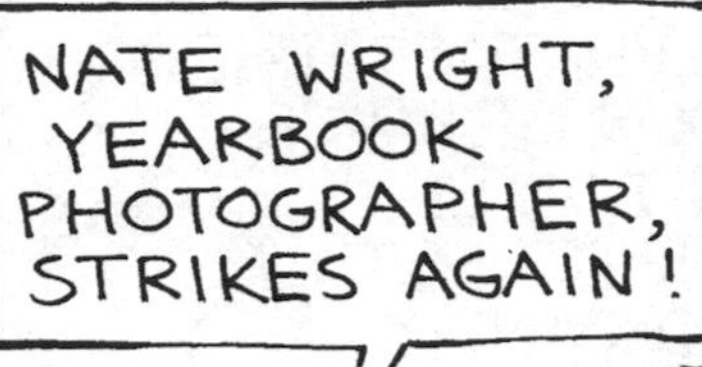
NATE WRIGHT, YEARBOOK PHOTOGRAPHER, STRIKES AGAIN!

POW!

STRUCK AGAIN.

EEEYAAWNN

CLICK!

WHAT I REALLY, REALLY NEED IS A CAMERA WITH A SILENCER.

HI, GORGEOUS! NATE WRIGHT, YEARBOOK PHOTOGRAPHER, HERE TO *CHUCKLE* "FOCUS" ON YOU!

WE PHOTOGRAPHERS ARE A VERY ROMANTIC GROUP! EVER HEAR THE EXPRESSION "SOMEDAY MY PRINTS WILL COME"?
HA
HA
HA

... AND SPEAKING OF PRINTS, HOW ABOUT WE STEP INTO MY DARK-ROOM AND... SEE WHAT "DEVELOPS"?

OH, WELL... HER LOSS.
HI, GORGEOUS!
HE'S RELOADING.
F-STOP THE INSANITY.

TRICIA! HEY, **TRICIA!**

HOW ABOUT A CANDID FOR THE YEARBOOK?

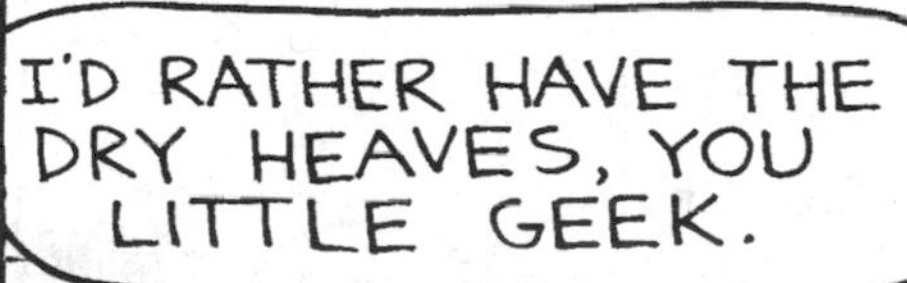
I'D RATHER HAVE THE DRY HEAVES, YOU LITTLE GEEK.

THAT WAS A LITTLE MORE CANDID THAN I HAD IN MIND.

HEY! WHAT ARE YOU DOING, KID?
ER... JUST TAKING PICTURES FOR THE YEARBOOK, GUYS!

YOU KNOW... CANDID SHOTS! PICTURES OF PEOPLE IN INTERESTING SITUATIONS... STUFF LIKE THAT.

YEAH? WE CAN GIVE YOU A HAND THERE!
GREAT!

CLICK!
RASH

HERE HE COMES!
SAY WHEN!

AAAAAND.. NOW!
beep

GOOD MORNING, MRS. GODFREY!
GOOD MORNING, NATE.
HERE'S THE HOMEWORK I FORGOT TO HAND IN YESTERDAY.
WHA-? NATE, THIS IS CHAPTER FIFTEEN!
YOU WERE SUPPOSED TO DO CHAPTER TWELVE!
WHOOPS

"WHOOPS"? IS THAT ALL YOU CAN.... OH, FOR GOODNESS SAKE! THERE'S CHEEZ DOODLE POWDER ALL OVER THIS HOMEWORK! IT STAINED MY BLOUSE!
UH... SORRY 'BOUT THAT..

?? WHAT'S THIS? IS THERE A DRAWING ON THE BACK OF THIS?
GULP! IS THERE?
DOODLING ON YOUR HOMEWORK? I'VE TOLD YOU NOT–
UH... I DIDN'T MEAN TO... UH... IT WAS JUST...
WAIT A MINUTE! IS THIS SUPPOSED TO BE ME??
DETENTION, NATE! NOW!!
beep

FORTY-THREE SECONDS!
A NEW RECORD!
OH, HOW I HATE HER.

MRS. GODFREY, WHY ARE YOU ALWAYS MAKING US MEMORIZE ALL THESE HISTORICAL DATES? WHY DO WE HAVE TO BE SO **EXACT** ABOUT IT?

I KNOW WHAT THE LOUISIANA PURCHASE WAS! I KNOW HOW IMPORTANT IT WAS! SO WHY DO I NEED TO MEMORIZE THE EXACT YEAR IT HAPPENED? WHY?... **WHY?**

IN CASE YOU END UP BEING TESTED ON IT.

DID YOU EVER STOP TO THINK ABOUT THE SIMILARITIES BETWEEN SCHOOL AND THE INSURANCE INDUSTRY?
Peirce

DO YOU THINK PEOPLE SEE ME IN A DIFFERENT LIGHT NOW?
WHATTA YA MEAN?

I MEAN, I'M MAIN-TAINING A "B" AVERAGE NOW! I'M GETTING GOOD GRADES! I'M PRACTICALLY ON THE HONOR ROLL!

BUT I DON'T WANT PEOPLE TO START THINKING OF ME AS SOME POINTY-HEADED, SUPER SMART INTELLECTUAL!

I THINK YOU'RE SAFE THERE.
THERE'S NO "Y" IN "EUROPE."

DOIN' THE MATH HOMEWORK? HEY, WHAT'D YOU GET FOR NUMBER FOUR?

YOU JUST WANT ME TO TELL YOU BECAUSE **YOU** HAVEN'T DONE IT YET.
YES I HAVE! I **HAVE**! I JUST WANT TO CHECK MY ANSWERS, THAT'S ALL!

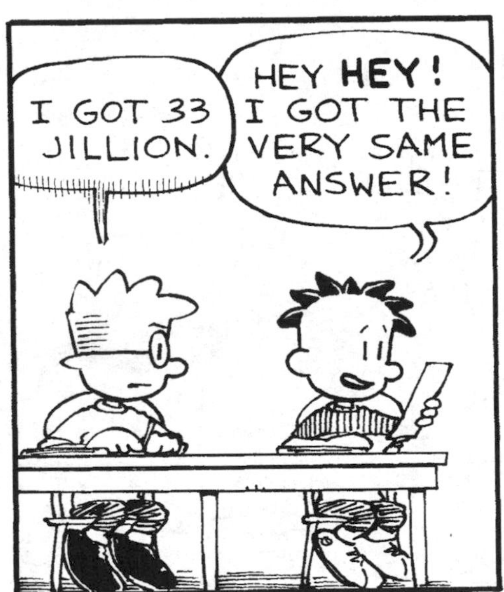
I GOT 33 JILLION.
HEY **HEY**! I GOT THE VERY SAME ANSWER!

YOU WOULD.
UM... HOW MANY ZEROS IN A JILLION AGAIN?
Peirce

I SPILLED ROOT BEER ON MY HOME-WORK BY ACCIDENT.

MAY I ASK **WHY** YOU WERE DRINKING **ROOT BEER** WHILE DOING YOUR **HOMEWORK?**

BECAUSE I RAN OUT OF "MOUNTAIN DEW."

DUH
MY SENTIMENTS EXACTLY.
Peirce

HOMEWORK, PLEASE, NATE.
HOMEWORK! RIGHT! UH... LET'S SEE HERE...

HANG ON A SEC... IT'S HERE **SOME**WHERE... IS THIS IT?... NO.... **DANG**! WHERE THE HECK **IS**....? A**HA**! **GOT** IT!
RUSTLE RUSTLE

I **KNEW** I HADN'T LEFT IT AT HOME!

PITY.
...AND **HEY**! **THERE'S** MY GUM!

NATE! WOULD IT BE ASKING TOO MUCH FOR YOU TO HAND IN HOMEWORK THAT'S NEAT AND CLEAN?

EVERY SINGLE PAPER HAS PIZZA GREASE ON IT, OR A SODA STAIN, OR... OR... WHATEVER THIS IS!
HMM... LEMME SEE...

OH, YEAH. THIS IS THE ONE I SNEEZED ON.

SNIFF! I JUST CAN'T SHAKE THIS COLD.
EXCUSE ME, CLASS, WHILE I GO WASH MY HANDS...
Peirce

WELL, GODFREY WON'T YELL AT ME WHEN I HAND IN THIS HOME-WORK! NO WRINKLES, NO RIPS, NO FOOD STAINS... IT'S PERFECT!

I EVEN PRINTED IT OUT ON THE COMPUTER, ON A BRAND-NEW CRISP SHEET OF...
OW! PAPER CUT!

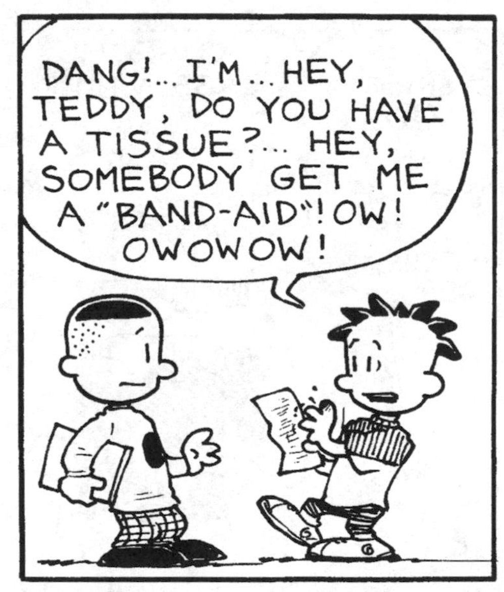
DANG!... I'M... HEY, TEDDY, DO YOU HAVE A TISSUE?... HEY, SOMEBODY GET ME A "BAND-AID"! OW! OWOWOW!

ARE THESE BLOOD STAINS?
I'M JINXED.

THAT DOES IT! THIS TIME SHE'S GONE TOO FAR!

IT'S NOT ENOUGH FOR MRS. GODFREY TO SCREAM AT ME BECAUSE MY HOMEWORK'S A LITTLE MESSY! NOW SHE'S ACTUALLY LOWERING MY GRADE!

OKAY, SO MY HOMEWORK HAD A FEW FOOD STAINS ON IT! FOR THAT SHE GIVES ME A D-MINUS?
F

THAT, AND THE FACT THAT YOU IDENTIFIED ROGER WILLIAMS AS THE POINT GUARD FOR THE SACRAMENTO KINGS.
WHAT, IS IT THE CLIPPERS? DANG! I SHOULD HAVE SAID CLIPPERS!
F
PEIRCE

NATE!
YIP!

WOULD YOU MIND EXPLAINING WHY YOU'RE BRINGING A ROCK INTO SCHOOL?!
IT'S A COUNTER-WEIGHT!
A COUNTER-WEIGHT.
SO I WON'T TIP OVER!

MY BACKPACK IS SO LOADED DOWN WITH HOMEWORK I CAN'T WALK NORMALLY!

IF I DON'T HOLD THIS ROCK OUT IN FRONT OF ME, I'LL TOPPLE OVER BACK-WARD!

NATE, THAT IS THE MOST RIDICULOUS THING I'VE EVER HEARD! DROP THAT ROCK! NOW!!
WONK!

WUMP!

I CAN SEE GET-TING DETENTION FOR THIS, BUT IF SHE STEPS ON ME, THAT'S WAY TOO HARSH.

HEY, NATE! I'M GOING TO THE DANCE COMMITTEE MEETING! WANNA JOIN ME?
THE DANCE COMMITTEE? ARE YOU OUT OF YOUR MIND, TEDDY?

I DON'T WANT TO SIT AROUND DECIDING WHAT COLOR CREPE PAPER TO HANG IN THE GYM, OR WHICH CHEESY LOCAL DJ WE'RE GONNA HIRE TO PLAY LAME TOP-40 MUSIC! NO, THANK YOU!
OKAY...

I'LL TELL JENNY, EMILY, TINA, MEGHAN, LISA, ASHLEY, HANNAH, LORI AND RACHEL NOT TO EXPECT YOU.

WHOA! WHOA! CHANGED MY MIND! CHANGED MY MIND!
DANCE FEVER.
Peirce

HI, JENNY! TEDDY AND I ARE HERE FOR THE DANCE COMMITTEE MEETING!
YOU?

YES, US! WHAT'S WRONG WITH THAT?
NOTHING'S WRONG WITH IT! IT'S JUST... WE'VE NEVER HAD ANY BOYS AT OUR MEETINGS!

YOU TWO WILL BE THE ONLY GUYS IN A ROOMFUL OF GIRLS.

ROWRR!
SUDDENLY I FEEL LIKE DANCING!

OKAY, LET'S START THE MEETING, GIRLS.
GIRLS AND GUYS!
DANCE
MMITTEE

TEDDY AND I WANT TO HELP MAKE THIS NEXT DANCE THE BEST EVER!
OH, PLEASE.

WE ALL KNOW THE TWO OF YOU ARE ONLY HERE BECAUSE YOU'RE TROLLING!

NOW WHAT DO WE DO?
UH... "TROLLING"? WHAT IS THIS "TROLLING"?
Peirce

ADMIT IT, NATE! YOU AND TEDDY HAVE NO INTEREST IN PLANNING THE DANCE!

YOU'RE JUST HERE FOR SOME **FACE TIME** WITH US **GIRLS**!
THAT'S NOT TRUE! WE HAVE **LOTS** OF GOOD IDEAS FOR THE...

...THE...

SORRY I'M LATE.
WHAT WAS I SAYING?
HEL- **LO**!
Peirce

OKAY, FIRST LET'S DECIDE WHAT THE THEME OF OUR DANCE SHOULD BE!
HOW'S **THIS** FOR A THEME:

THE 6TH GRADE GIRLS ACTUALLY **DANCE** WITH THE 6TH GRADE BOYS, INSTEAD OF THROWING THEMSELVES AT THE **7TH** AND **8TH** GRADE BOYS AND LEAVING THE **6TH** GRADE BOYS STANDING AROUND EATING SOUR CREAM AND ONION CHIPS AT THE **SNACK TABLE!**

OKAY, MOVING RIGHT ALONG...
I DON'T THINK THAT'LL FIT ON A POSTER, MAN.
Peirce

OKAY, THE THEME OF THE DANCE WILL BE "STUPID CUPID." ANY OTHER QUESTIONS?
YES, I HAVE A QUESTION!

JENNY, WILL YOU GO TO THE "STUPID CUPID" DANCE WITH ME?

NO.
RACHEL, WILL **YOU** GO TO THE DANCE WITH ME?

HA HA. RIGHT.
LORI, WILL **YOU** GO TO...
HE'S GOING "AROUND THE HORN."
Peirce

★☆★☆★☆★☆★☆★
Time For Another Scintillating Edition OF...
FACULTY INTERVIEW!
with your host: CHIP CHIPSON!

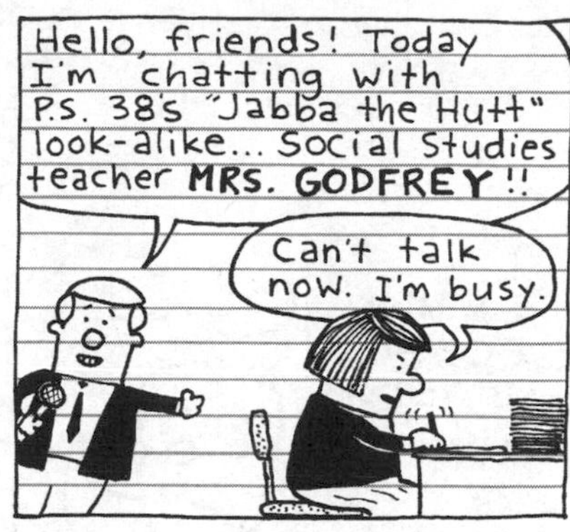
Hello, friends! Today I'm chatting with P.S. 38's "Jabba the Hutt" look-alike... Social Studies teacher MRS. GODFREY!!
Can't talk now. I'm busy.

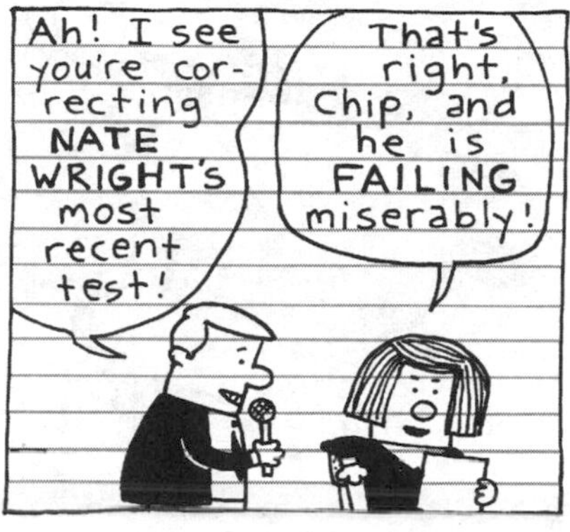
Ah! I see you're correcting NATE WRIGHT's most recent test!
That's right, Chip, and he is FAILING miserably!

And yet... you seem HAPPY about that!
OF COURSE I'm happy about it! That's what I WANTED to happen!

I... I don't understand.
I told Nate to study Chapter Three! Then I tested him on Chapter TWELVE!

But... that's totally UNFAIR!
Exactly! That's how he'll LEARN: by absorbing DEFEAT after devastating DEFEAT!

You've got to BREAK kids' spirits while they're young, Chip! Sure, it may seem cruel... but deep down they LOVE you for it!

OH, HOW I LOATHE HER.
JUST AN OBSERVATION: THERE WERE NO MATADORS AT THE BATTLE OF BULL RUN.

MR. GALVIN, HOW COME WE NEVER DO ANYTHING COOL IN SCIENCE?
"COOL"?

LIKE CLONING! CAN'T WE TRY TO CLONE SOMETHING? PLEASE? LET'S CLONE SOMETHING!

OR SOMEONE! HEY! I'LL VOLUNTEER! I'D GET CLONED IN A HEARTBEAT! LET'S CLONE ME!

SPEAKING FOR THE FACULTY, NATE, ONE OF YOU IS QUITE ENOUGH.
I'LL SEND MY CLONE TO SOCIAL STUDIES, WHILE I WATCH CARTOONS IN THE A.V. ROOM!
Peirce

THE MORE I THINK ABOUT IT, THE MORE I LIKE THE IDEA OF CLONING MYSELF!
NATE...

...AND THE BEST PART IS, ALL WE NEED TO GET STARTED IS A TINY SAMPLE OF... OF...

AACHOOOOOO

...MY DNA.
I'VE HAD EIGHT COLDS SINCE SEPTEMBER.
WIPE!
Peirce

...BUT WHY **CAN'T** I CLONE MYSELF?
NATE, WHAT YOU'RE TALKING ABOUT IS **SCIENCE FICTION**!

NOT ONLY IS CLONING OF HUMAN BEINGS STILL ONLY THEORETICAL, THERE ARE MANY **OTHER** ISSUES OF...
AH, AH! I KNOW WHAT YOU'RE GOING TO SAY, MR. GALVIN!

...AND I ASSURE YOU I HAVE NO PROBLEMS AT ALL WITH THE **ETHICAL RAMIFICATIONS** OF CLONING MYSELF!

WHY DOESN'T THAT SURPRISE ME?
NOW IF **MRS. GODFREY** WANTED TO GET CLONED!... **THEN** WE'D HAVE A PROBLEM!
Peirce

1.) Carl is taking a math test. There are 10 questions which take 30 seconds each; 15 questions which take 40 seconds each; and 12 questions which take two minutes each.

Carl pauses for 5 seconds between questions. In addition, he sharpens his pencil twice, which takes 20 seconds each time. The test begins promptly at 10:00 am. When Carl hands in his completed test,

what time is it?

? ? ?
10
15
+ 12
37
300 secs.
5 mins.

40
x 15
200
400
600 secs.
10 mins.
36
x 5
180
+ 40 secs.
3 mins.
40 secs.
120
x 12
240
1200
1440 secs.
24
60 | 1440
120
240
600
300
1440
180
2520
39 min.

YAAAAAAAH!

TICK
TICK
TICK
TICK
TICK
TICK
TICK
PRINCIPAL

WHAT'S THAT?
MY BOOK REPORT!

HOW COME IT'S SO LONG, GINA? IT HAD TO BE ONLY TWO PAGES!
I KNOW! BUT I WANTED TO DO MORE!

TWO PAGES SIMPLY AREN'T ENOUGH FOR ME TO SAY EVERY-THING I WANT TO SAY!

I CAN SAY EVERY-THING I WANT TO SAY IN TWO WORDS.
Peirce

HERE'S MY BOOK REPORT, MRS. GODFREY!

PLEASE NOTE THE SLEEK PLASTIC BINDER, THE MUSEUM-QUALITY PAPER, AND THE FULL-COLOR TITLE PAGE!

ARE YOU FAMILIAR WITH THE EXPRESSION "PUTTING LIPSTICK ON A PIG"?

I AM NOW.
Peirce

UH... MRS. GODFREY? WHEN YOU HANDED BACK OUR REPORTS, MINE DIDN'T HAVE A GRADE ON IT.
YES, I KNOW.
S. GODFREY

IF YOU'RE NOT GOING TO PUT ANY EFFORT INTO WRITING YOUR REPORTS, I'M NOT GOING TO PUT ANY EFFORT INTO **GRADING** THEM.

MRS. GODFREY

SOMETHING JUST HAPPENED THAT'S EITHER VERY, VERY GOOD OR VERY, VERY BAD.
Peirce

YOU'LL HAVE 45 MINUTES TO COMPLETE THIS TEST.

OKAY, HERE WE GO! NUMBER ONE!...
I'LL COME BACK TO THAT ONE.

NUMBER TWO...
UMM.... I'LL COME BACK TO THAT ONE, TOO.

NUMBER THREE...
HEY, WHAT IS THIS? I HARDLY KNOW ANY OF THESE!
mumble
huh?
?
?
?
grumble

WHOOPS! MY APOLOGIES, PEOPLE! I GAVE YOU THE WRONG TEST!

I GAVE YOU THE TEST FOR MY OTHER CLASS! THEY'RE TWO CHAPTERS AHEAD OF YOU!

HERE'S THE RIGHT TEST!
AS I SAID, YOU HAVE 45 MINUTES.

OKAY! NUMBER ONE!

CAN I HAVE THE OTHER TEST BACK?
Peirce

MR. ROSA! LITTLE HELP!
OOP!

DRIBBA
DRIBBA
DRIBBA
DRIBBA
DRIBBA
DRIBBA
DRIBBA
DRIBBA
DRIBBA
DRIBBA

SWISH!

WOW!
SECOND TEAM ALL-STATE, 1974.
Peirce

NATE! REMEMBER WHEN WE FOUND OUT THAT MR. ROSA IS GOOD AT BASKETBALL? IT GAVE ME AN IDEA!

A KIDS VS. TEACHERS BASKETBALL GAME! WOULDN'T THAT BE A **BLAST**?

NATE! I SAID, DON'T YOU THINK THAT WOULD BE A BLAST?

NATE?
I WANT IT UNDERSTOOD I REFUSE TO PLAY "IN-YOUR-FACE" DEFENSE AGAINST MRS. GODFREY.
Peirce

NATE?
UH-HUH?

ABOUT YOUR POSTER FOR THE KIDS VS. TEACHERS BASKET-BALL GAME...
YEAH?

IS IT REALLY NECESSARY TO REFER TO THE TEACHERS AS THE "EVIL EMPIRE"?
WELL, THAT DEPENDS. IS MRS. GODFREY PLAYING FOR YOU GUYS?
SAT

UH... YES.
THEN YES!
Peirce

MR. STAPLES! ARE YOU PLAYING IN THE KIDS VS. TEACHERS BASKETBALL GAME?
I SURE AM!

ARE YOU ANY GOOD?
WELL, IT'S BEEN AWHILE SINCE I PLAYED, BUT I THINK I'LL DO ALL RIGHT.

I JUST HOPE MY SHOOTING ISN'T AFFECTED BY MY... AHEM!... 1979 NCAA DIVISION 2 CHAMPIONSHIP RING!

WH... WHA... WHA...
I WAS ONLY THE TEAM STATISTICIAN, BUT I WON'T TELL HIM THAT.
Peirce

CLAP CLAP CLAP
KIDS VS. TEACHERS! LET'S GET IT ON!
LOOK AT THE SIZE OF THIS **CROWD!**
CLAP CLAP CLAP CLAP CLAP CLAP CLAP CLAP CLAP

CLAP CLAP
HERE THEY COME! MR. ROSA... MR. GALVIN... MS. LA CHANCE...
CLAP CLAP CLAP

GASP!

THERE'S NOTHING LIKE THE SIGHT OF MRS. GODFREY IN GYM SHORTS TO SUCK THE LIFE OUT OF A ROOM.
DO WE HAVE ANY MAALOX IN THE FIRST AID KIT?
Peirce

COACH! YOU'RE PLAYING IN THE KIDS VS. TEACHERS GAME?
OF COURSE! I'M A TEACHER, AREN'T I?

WELL...
SORT OF.
SORT OF?

IN CASE YOU'VE FORGOTTEN, I DO TEACH HEALTH!
OH, WE HAVEN'T FORGOTTEN!
MMPH!

SIGH...
REMEMBER HIS LECTURE: "PUBERTY, THE MAGICAL MYSTERY TOUR"?
BARELY! I WAS ASLEEP FOR MOST OF IT!
HA HA HA HA HA HA HA HA HA HA HA HEE HEE HEE HE HA HA HA
Peirce

SAY, MRS. GODFREY... HOW MANY LETTERS IN THE ALPHABET?
WHY... TWENTY-SIX, OF COURSE.

NOPE. ONLY TWENTY-FIVE.
SWISH!

'CAUSE YOU GOT NO "D."

WORD!
THAT FELT GOOOOOOD!

HERE COMES MR. ROSA! HE'S MADE HIS LAST FIVE SHOTS!
MESS UP HIS RHYTHM! FIND A WAY TO BREAK HIS CONCENTRATION!

HI, MR. ROSA.
HELLO, NATE.

PICASSO'S OKAY, BUT HE CAN'T HOLD A CANDLE TO LEROY NEIMAN.

L... L... LE... LEROY... N... N... NEI...
THANKS. I'LL TAKE THAT!
Peirce

WATCH ME "UP-FAKE" MR. GALVIN INTO THE BLEACHERS!

IT'S HARD TO "UP-FAKE" SOMEBODY WHO LOST HIS REFLEXES DURING THE NIXON ADMINISTRATION.
Peirce

GO IN FOR ME, FRANCIS.
WHAT'S WRONG? DID YOU GET HURT?
CATS 7

I JUST NEED TO TAKE A SHOWER, THAT'S ALL.
A **SHOWER?** THE GAME'S NOT EVEN **HALF OVER!**

THIS IS AN EMERGENCY.

HE GOT A DROP OF MRS. GODFREY'S SWEAT ON HIM.
I'M UNCLEAN.
RUB RUB RUB

SHOOT, BILL! SHOOT!

WHAP!

LOOKS LIKE YOUR "BILL" WAS JUST VETOED!
CHUCKLE!

IS THERE ANYTHING WORSE THAN GETTING TRASH-TALKED BY A SOCIAL STUDIES TEACHER?
Peirce

I DON'T BELIEVE THIS! WE'RE GOING TO **LOSE**! TO THE **TEACHERS**!
WE CAN STILL WIN!
CATS
0
6

IT AIN'T OVER 'TIL THE FAT LADY SINGS!

SWISH!
0

NA NA NAAA NA... NA NA NAAA NA... HEY HEY HEY... GOODBYE...
CATS
Peirce

WHAT'S **THAT** SUPPOSED TO MEAN?
JUST WHAT IT SAYS!
ANYTHING FOR $1

FOR ONLY A DOLLAR, I CAN SEARCH MY VAST INVENTORY FOR ANYTHING THE BUYER WANTS!
ANYTHING? YUH, **RIGHT!**

HERE'S A BUCK! GIMME A DOZEN DONUTS! **JELLY-FILLED!**
A DOZEN JELLY-FILLED! COMIN' UP!
RUSTLE RUSTLE
VOILA!
WOW!
HEY, THAT'S **GOOD!** LET **ME** TRY!
CERTAINLY, MY GOOD MAN!

WHAT CAN I GET YOU FOR **YOUR** DOLLAR?

A 10-DOLLAR BILL.
A 10-DOLLAR BILL! COMIN' RIGHT...

CLOSED

Investigative Reporter
CHIP CHIPSON
presents:
BURNING ISSUES!

Friends, today's "burning issue" is BULLYING! And here to discuss it is celebrity psychologist DR. WARREN FUZZY!
Chip, bullying is the scourge of our schools!
BONK!

We all remember what it's like to be bullied! We've all felt POWERLESS!

...but what we DON'T REALIZE is how powerless the BULLIES feel!

The BULLIES feel power-less??
Right, Chip! That's why they're bullies!

They're COMPENSATING for their underlying sense of inadequacy! Underneath, they're COWARDS!

Once we know that, we can STAND UP to the bullies and STOP the cycle of bullying!

NATE.
HMM?
I'M WATCHING YOU, MISTER.
Does that really work?
Unless they're teachers. Then you just live in fear.
Peirce

LOOK! WE MUST BE HAVING A FILM-STRIP TODAY!
YESSSS! A FILM-STRIP!

NATE, WILL YOU RUN THE PROJECTOR?
ME? I GOTTA RUN THE PROJECTOR?

BUT THEN I WON'T BE ABLE TO SLEE...!

PARDON?
...TO SLA-... SLOO... SLI... SLIDE! TO SLIDE INTO MY SEAT AND GIVE THE FILMSTRIP MY FULL ATTENTION!
Peirce

KLIK!

KLIK!

KLIK
KLIK
KLIK
KLIK
KLIK

IK
LIK
LIK
KLIK
KLIK
KLI
Z

MY REPORT TODAY IS ON THE REPUBLIC OF CAMERON, WHICH IS A PRETTY COOL NAME FOR A COUNTRY, IF YOU ASK ME.

I MEAN, I'VE GOT A **COUSIN** NAMED CAMERON. IT'S LIKE... "HI, I'VE GOT A WHOLE **COUNTRY** NAMED AFTER ME!" ISN'T THAT—

IT'S CAME**ROON**, NATE. YOU'RE LEAVING OUT A LETTER.

O.
Peirce

NICE MOVE, NATE! DOING YOUR REPORT ON THE REPUBLIC OF CAMERON INSTEAD OF CAMEROON!
HA HA HEE HEE

SO? IT WAS A MISTAKE, THAT'S ALL! AREN'T I ENTITLED TO ONE MISTAKE?

ONE MISTAKE, YES! BUT YOU'VE DONE THIS BEFORE!

REMEMBER HIS REPORT ON THE "WHIG" PARTY?
WHEN HE BROUGHT IN THAT TOUPEE?

TEACHERS' LOUNGE! SEE THAT? **TEACHERS' LOUNGE!**

HOW COME **THEY** GET A ROOM TO HANG OUT IN AND **WE DON'T**?

WE'RE THE ONES WHO REALLY **NEED** A PLACE LIKE THAT! **WE'RE** THE ONES WHO ARE UNDER ALL THE **STRESS!**

WHILE THEY'RE IN THERE EATING DONUTS AND TAKING CATNAPS, WE'RE OUT HERE RUNNING AROUND LIKE RATS IN A MAZE!

IS IT ASKING TOO MUCH FOR US TO HAVE A PLACE FOR OURSELVES?...WHERE WE CAN **RELAX** FOR A CHANGE?

JUST GIVE US A **ROOM**, THAT'S ALL! I MEAN, DON'T WE **DESERVE** THAT? **DON'T WE??**

ALL I WANT IS A LITTLE PEACE AND~

QUIET
PLEASE

TEDDY AND MEGHAN...
SHEILA AND JULIE...
MARK AND APRIL...
NATE AND ARTUR...
JANELLE AND ZACK...
FRANCIS AND EVA...

ARRRGH! I CAN'T BELIEVE I'M DOING THE RE-SEARCH PROJECT WITH ARTUR!
YOU'RE LUCKY, NATE! YOU'LL GET AN "A" FOR SURE!
F

WHO CARES? I'LL BE WORKING WITH MY ARCH-ENEMY!
I THOUGHT YOU AND ARTUR WERE FRIENDS NOW!
F

THAT'S A SHAM, FRANCIS! ARTUR'S ONLY PRETEND-ING TO BE MY FRIEND! HE'S A TWO-FACE! HE'S A TOTAL PHONY!

HALLO.
HEEEEEEY! ARTUR, OL' BUDDY, OL' PAL O' MINE!
F
Peirce

IS GOOD WE ARE DOING RESEARCH PROJECT TOGETHER, NATE.
OH, YEAH. IT'S GREAT.

SO. WE START ON THE WORKING, THEN?
WHAT, **NOW**? WE JUST **SAT DOWN**! WE CAN'T START WORKING **RIGHT AWAY**!

FIRST WE'VE GOT TO HANG OUT FOR A WHILE! SHOOT THE BREEZE! TALK ABOUT MRS. GODFREY!
AH! OKAY.

SHE IS EXCELLENT TEACHER, YES? I REALLY LIKE HER.
ARTUR, ARTUR, ARTUR...
Peirce

TEN PAGES! I CAN'T BELIEVE GODFREY EXPECTS US TO WRITE **TEN PAGES**!
NATE. WHY ALWAYS DO YOU COMPLAIN ABOUT MRS. GODFREY?

WHY? BECAUSE THAT'S WHAT WE **DO**, ARTUR! WE'RE **STUDENTS**! STUDENTS COMPLAIN ABOUT TEACHERS!

YOU TRY IT, ARTUR! COMPLAIN ABOUT A TEACHER! **ANY** TEACHER!
CANNOT THINK OF ANY-THING BAD TO SAY.

I'M HAVING A HARD TIME FORMING A POSITIVE WORKING RELATIONSHIP WITH MY RESEARCH PARTNER.
Peirce

LOOK, ARTUR, THERE'S NOTHING WRONG WITH RAGGING ON A TEACHER EVERY ONCE IN A WHILE! IT'S NORMAL! IT'S **HEALTHY!**
IT IS?

YES! GIVE IT A TRY, ARTUR! THINK UP A NICKNAME FOR MRS. GODFREY! YOU CAN DO IT! IT'S **EASY!**
A NICK-NAME?

UMMMMM... "MA'AM"?

I HAVE MUCH WORK TO DO.
MRS. MA'AM!
Peirce

WHAT **IS** IT WITH ARTUR?
WHATTAYA MEAN?

YESTERDAY I TRIED TO GET HIM TO BUST ON MRS. GODFREY, AND YOU KNOW WHAT?... HE **WOULDN'T DO IT!**
SO? HE'S NICE, THAT'S ALL!

HE'S TOO NICE FOR HIS OWN **GOOD!** WOULD IT KILL HIM TO BE A LITTLE... JUST A LITTLE MORE...

...MORE LIKE YOU?
YES! **YES!...** **THANK** YOU!
Peirce

DID YOU KNOW THAT ARTUR IS TOTALLY INCAPABLE OF SAYING ANYTHING NEGATIVE ABOUT A TEACHER?
THAT'S ARTUR!
YEAH, HE'S SO NICE!

HE'S SMART, TOO! AND FUNNY!
HE'S PERFECT!

WELL, HE'S NOT **PERFECT**! NOBODY'S **PERFECT**!
I AM!

I JUST HAVE THE GOOD SENSE NOT TO GO AROUND **FLAUNTING** IT!
YOU CAN SAY THAT AGAIN.
Peirce

ARTUR IS HOPELESS! I'M GOING TO TUTOR HIM.
TUTOR HIM? IN WHAT?

CRITICIZING PEOPLE! ARTUR HAS NO CLUE HOW TO RIP A TEACHER! HE'S UNSCHOOLED IN THE FINE ART OF THE PUTDOWN!

SO YOU'RE GOING TO TEACH ARTUR HOW TO SAY INSULTING THINGS ABOUT OTHER PEOPLE.
EXACTLY!

YOU'RE SUCH AN IDIOT.
RIGHT, STUFF LIKE THAT. ONLY MORE IMAGINATIVE.
PEIRCE

YOU KNOW WHAT YOUR PROBLEM IS, ARTUR?
PROBLEM? NO.

YOU NEVER SAY ANYTHING BAD ABOUT ANYONE! EVERYBODY THINKS YOU'RE A GOODY TWO-SHOES!
WHAT IS GOODY TWO-SHOES?

YOU KNOW... GOOD! TOO GOOD! ANNOYINGLY GOOD! OBNOXIOUSLY GOOD!
AH.

SO?... WHAT DO YOU SAY TO THAT?
THANK YOU VERY MUCH!
Peirce

ARTUR, I'M NOT BUYING THIS "NICE KID" ROUTINE OF YOURS!
ROUTINE?

RIGHT! EVERYBODY KNOWS HOW YOU NEVER SAY ANY-THING BAD ABOUT ANY-ONE...
BECAUSE... DO NOT HAVE ANYTHING BAD TO SAY!

BUT YOU MUST THINK BAD THINGS EVERY ONCE IN A WHILE, RIGHT? DON'T YOU AT LEAST THINK BAD THOUGHTS ABOUT SOME PEOPLE?

AM BEGINNING TO.
Peirce

COME **ON**, ARTUR! DEEP DOWN YOU **WANT** TO BUST ON MRS. GODFREY! LET IT OUT, MAN!
STOP IT, NATE. NO!

BUT IT'S **EASY**! LISTEN, I'LL DEMONSTRATE:

MRS. GODFREY IS SO HUGE, SHE HAS HER OWN OZONE LAYER!

...WHICH YOU'D THINK WOULD MAKE IT DIFFICULT FOR HER TO SNEAK UP SO QUIETLY LIKE THAT.
Peirce

SO?... DID YOU SUCCEED IN GETTING ARTUR TO CRITICIZE MRS. GODFREY?
NOPE.

I FINALLY REALIZED IT WASN'T AN **ACT!** ARTUR IS **LITERALLY** INCAPABLE OF SAYING AN UNKIND WORD ABOUT ANYONE!

HE'S A NICE KID. HE'S PROBABLY THE NICEST KID I'VE EVER MET.

OH, HOW I HATE HIM.
Peirce

SOUNDS of the GAME

squeak
squeak
squeak
squeak
squeak
squeak

TAP TAP!
TWEEE EEET
DOOF!

DRIBBA
DRIBBA
DRIBBA
DRIBBA
DRIBBA
DRIBBA
DRIBBA

DRIBBA DRIBBA DRIBBA DRIBBA
DRIBBA DRIBBA DRIBBA DRIBBA
DRIBBA DRIBBA DRIBBA
DRIBBA DRIBBA DRIBBA
DRIBBA DRIBBA
DRIBBA
DRIBBA
DRIBBA
DRIBBA
DRIBBA
DRIBBA
DRIBBA
ZING!

BONK!
!

SLURP

MRS. SHIPULSKI, I'M WORKING ON THE NEXT ISSUE OF "CLASSROOM CHATTERS," AND...
HOLD IT RIGHT THERE, NATE!

I WILL **NOT** BE INTERVIEWED FOR YOUR **GOSSIP COLUMN**! YOU'VE MISQUOTED ME **TOO MANY TIMES**!
"SHIPULSKI MUM ON RUMORS."

RUMORS? WAIT A MINUTE! YOU DIDN'T SAY ANYTHING ABOUT...
"SHIPULSKI PLEADS IGNORANCE AS SCANDAL INTENSIFIES."

SCANDAL?? SCANDAL??
"SECRETARY SNAPS."
Peirce

MRS. SHIPULSKI, CAN I INTERVIEW PRINCIPAL NICHOLS?
HE'S BUSY RIGHT NOW, NATE.
MRS. SHIPULSKI

DOING WHAT?
THAT'S **HIS** BUSINESS.
SOMETHING SECRET?
IT'S NOT **SECRET**, IT'S JUST...
WHAT'S HE HIDING?
MRS. SHIPULSKI

HE'S NOT HIDING **ANYTHING**!
SO HE HAS NOTHING TO HIDE?
OF **COURSE** NOT!
HE **DOESN'T** HAVE NOTHING TO HIDE?

YES!... NO!... SPUTTER!...
"PRINCIPAL LURES LOYAL SECRETARY INTO WEB OF LIES."
MRS. SHIPULSKI
Peirce

NATE, ISN'T THERE SOMEPLACE YOU NEED TO BE?
NOPE! THE ACTION'S RIGHT HERE!
MRS. SHIPULSKI

"ACTION"?
YOU'RE THE PRINCIPAL'S SECRETARY, MRS. SHIPULSKI! EVERYTHING GOES THROUGH **YOU**!

IT'S NOT AS EXCITING AS YOU MIGHT THINK.
NOT ON THE **SURFACE**! BUT UNDER**NEATH**, THIS SCHOOL IS A **HOTBED** OF DYSFUNCTION AND INTRIGUE!

MRS. SHIPULSKI? HAS MY PIZZA ARRIVED YET?
NO, SIR.
AH HA!
MRS. SHIPULSKI
Peirce

EEEEOOWWRRRR

CHUCKLE
HA HA
MMPH
HEE HEE
SNICKER

BEEEYOWWRRRR

HA HA HA HA
HA HA HA HA

NATE! WHAT IS GOING ON?
ER... MY... MY STOMACH WAS GROWLING!

WELL, YOUR STOMACH IS DISRUPTING THE CLASS! DO SOMETHING ABOUT IT!

RUSTLE
RUSTLE
CRINKLE
MUNCH
SLURP

GOT ANY SALT?

WHAT?

DETENTION
EEEYOWWWRRRR...
MRS. CZERWICKI
Peirce

SNIFF!
I SMELL
DANGER.
WHATTAYA
MEAN,
YOU
SMELL
DANGER?

SNIFF!
I JUST
DO.
THAT'S
RIDICULOUS,
NATE! HOW
CAN YOU
SMELL
DANGER?

WHEN DANGER JUST
POLISHED OFF AN ONION
BAGEL AND A HAZELNUT
DECAF IN THE TEACHERS
LOUNGE, IT'S NOT THAT
TOUGH.
Peirce

YOU KNOW WHAT MRS. GODFREY SAID THIS MORNING? SHE...
SNIFF! HOLD IT, TEDDY. SHE'S COMING.

HUH? NO, SHE ISN'T!
TRUST ME. *SNIFF!* SHE'S ABOUT TO COME AROUND THE CORNER.

WOW! NATE, THAT WAS...
TALK TO THE NOSE!
Peirce

FRANCIS! DID YOU KNOW THAT NATE CAN **SMELL** MRS. GODFREY FROM A MILE AWAY?
NOT JUST MRS. GODFREY! **ANY** TEACHER!

ALL TEACHERS HAVE THEIR OWN UNIQUE **SCENTS**, MY FRIENDS! AND THANKS TO MY AMAZING SENSE OF SMELL, I KNOW 'EM ALL!

MR. GALVIN, FOR EXAMPLE, IS A BEWITCHING BLEND OF CHALK, RUBBING ALCOHOL, TEABERRY GUM, FORMALDEHYDE, SHOE POLISH, "OLD SPICE" AND UNIDENTIFIED!

"UNIDENTIFIED"?
I DON'T LIKE THE SOUND OF THAT.
I'VE NARROWED IT DOWN. IT'S EITHER B.O. OR SOME KIND OF DEAD ANIMAL.
PEIRCE

LET'S PUT YOUR SENSE OF SMELL TO THE TEST!
YEAH, NATE! SEE IF YOU CAN IDENTIFY THE TEACHERS AS THEY GO BY!
F

SNIFF
SNIFF
SNIFF

HI, MS. BRINDLE!
UH... HELLO, NATE.

WELL, **DUH**! SHE'S THE "**LIFE SKILLS**" TEACHER!
YEAH, EVEN **I** COULD SMELL THE CINNAMON!
OK... GRANTED, THAT WAS A LAY-UP.
Peirce

OK, HERE COMES ANOTHER TEACHER!
YEAH, NATE! "NAME THAT TEACHER!"
SNIFF SNIFF

HMM... I'M GETTING A DISTINCT WHIFF OF ROSE PETALS... *SNIFF!* ...SO IT'S GOT TO BE MS. LA CHANCE!

HELLO, BOYS.

MR. STAPLES MIGHT WANT TO CONSIDER USING SOAP THAT'S A BIT MORE MACHO.
Peirce

SNIFF! I'M GETTING A WHIFF OF ACRYLIC PAINT, CLAY AND RUBBER CEMENT! MR. ROSA MUST BE CLOSE BY!
CORRECT!

BUT... *SNIFF!*... THERE'S SOMETHING **ELSE!** ... I'M SMELLING **MRS. GODFREY'S** SCENT ON MR. ROSA! WHICH CAN ONLY MEAN THAT...

... MR. ROSA AND MRS. GODFREY ARE HAVING AN AFFAIR!!

OR, THERE COULD BE ANOTHER EXPLANATION...
PLEASE, TEDDY. I'M THE EXPERT HERE.
Peirce

SCHOOL BUS
HEY.
HEY. CRUNCH

BACON?
YUP. CHOMP I'M EATING BREAKFAST ON THE RUN.

I WAS UP SO LATE FINISHING THIS STUPID SOCIAL STUDIES REPORT THAT I OVERSLEPT THIS MORNING!

YOU'RE GETTING BACON GREASE ALL OVER IT!
MUNCH SO WHAT?

IT'S DONE, THAT'S WHAT MATTERS! WHO CARES ABOUT A FEW GREASE STAINS?
SNIFF SNIFF

!
CHOMPF!
GULP MUNCH NARF NARF NARF CHOMP
BURP!

WACKY THING HAPPENED AT THE BUS STOP THIS MORNING...
I SMELL BACON.

I AM **SO READY** FOR TODAY'S SOCIAL STUDIES FINAL! I'VE BEEN CRAMMING FOR **DAYS**!
STOP

ASK ME ANY-THING!
OK... WHEN WILLIAM HENRY HARRISON RAN FOR PRESIDENT, WHAT WAS HIS CAMPAIGN SLOGAN?

HA! IT'S A TRICK QUESTION! WILLIAM HENRY HARRISON **NEVER RAN** FOR PRESIDENT!

UH... RIGHT?
YOU'VE STILL GOT 40 MINUTES.
Peirce

READY?...1620.
CHRISTOPHER COLUMBUS.
1803.
BOSTON TEA PARTY.
1861.
THE ALAMO.
1770.
MISSOURI COMPROMISE.

12.
12?

12... LET'S SEE HERE...
I WAS PREDICTING YOUR SCORE.
Peirce

WRITE
WRITE
WRITE
WRITE
WRITE
WRITE
WRITE
WRITE
WRITE

WRITE
WRITE
WRITE
WRITE
RITE
WRITE
WRITE
WRITE
WRITE
WRITE
WRITE

HOW'S THE TEST GOING, NATE?
GROANNN..
Peirce

NATE! HOW'D YOU DO ON THE TEST?
BAD

HOW BAD?
HOW SHOULD I KNOW?

WELL, DID YOU **FINISH** IT?
NOPE

IT FINISHED ME.
Peirce

HI, BUTTHEAD!
HI, UGLY!

HI, PIZZA FACE!
HI, PENCIL NECK!

HI, FISH BREATH!
HI, PEA BRAIN!
HA
HA
HA
HA
HA
HA
HA

HI, GEEK BOY!
HELLO, CLUELESS!
HA
HA
HA
HA
HA
HA
HA
HA

HI, BANANA NOSE!
HI, SQUIRREL TEETH!
HA
HA
HA
HA

HELLO, BOYS.
HI, FATSO!

DETENTION
HI STUPID
Peirce

HEY, LOOK WHAT I'VE GOT! THE BRAND-NEW EDITION OF THE "BOOK OF FACTS"!
OH, NO.

BEFORE YOU SAY ANYTHING MORE, FRANCIS, **PROMISE** ME YOU'RE NOT GOING TO BORE ME TO THE POINT OF INSANITY BY READING OUT LOUD FROM THAT **BOOK** ALL DAY!

SORRY. I CAN'T PROMISE THAT.

SAY, HERE'S A LITTLE-KNOWN FACT ABOUT SOLAR ECLIPSES! DID YOU KNOW THAT TOTAL SOLAR ECLIPSES ACTUALLY TAKE PLACE NEARLY AS OFTEN AS
SOMEBODY SHOOT ME.

WANNA HEAR A FASCINATING FACT?
IF I MUST.

WALKING AT A CONSTANT RATE OF 3.5 MILES PER HOUR, IT WOULD TAKE OVER 3,000 YEARS TO REACH THE SUN!
WOW! I CAN'T BELIEVE THAT!

WELL, IT'S TRUE! IT SAYS SO RIGHT HERE IN...
NO, NO! I CAN'T ACCEPT THAT! I NEED PROOF!

PROOF?
THE SUN'S THAT WAY. I'LL TIME YOU.
PEIRCE

HERE'S ANOTHER GEM FROM THE "BOOK OF FACTS"! DID YOU KNOW THAT...
NO! NO MORE GEMS! THROW THAT STUPID BOOK AWAY!

HEY, JUST BECAUSE YOU DON'T HAVE AN IN-QUISITIVE MIND DOESN'T MEAN THIS BOOK IS STUPID!

A BOOK LIKE THIS CAN COME IN VERY HANDY!
OKAY, OKAY, MAYBE YOU'RE RIGHT. LEMME SEE IT.

WAP!
Peirce

HERE'S A LITTLE-KNOWN FACT ABOUT ZEBRAS! DID YOU KNOW...
HOLD IT, **HOLD** IT! LET ME GIVE **YOU** A LITTLE-KNOWN FACT!

"LITTLE-KNOWN FACTS" ARE **CALLED** "LITTLE-KNOWN FACTS" BECAUSE SO **LITTLE** IS **KNOWN** ABOUT THEM!

...AND **WHY** IS SO LITTLE KNOWN ABOUT THEM?
BECAUSE NOBODY CARES!!

AND **WHY** DOES NOBODY CARE? BECAUSE, ACCORDING TO THE "BOOK OF FACTS," MOST PEOPLE USE ONLY **10%** OF THEIR BRAIN CAPAC
MAKE HIM STOP.
?
Peirce

SHEILA! YOU'RE THE CAPTAIN OF THE CHEERLEADING TEAM, RIGHT?
RIGHT.

WE'VE GOT A TOURNA-MENT TOMORROW, AND I WAS WON-DERING...
YOU WANT US TO CHEER AT A CHESS MEET?

NOW, NOW! I KNOW YOU'VE NEVER DONE IT BEFORE, BUT WHAT IF SOMEONE WROTE OUT A FEW CHESS CHEERS FOR YOU TO LEARN?

"CHESS CHEERS"?
HACK 'IM, WHACK 'IM, FIGHT, FIGHT, FIGHT! TAKE HIS BISHOP WITH YOUR KNIGHT!
Peirce

SIGH ANOTHER CHESS MEET. I GOTTA SAY, I'M NOT TOO FIRED UP FOR THIS ONE.
YEAH, ARTUR WAS SAYING THE SAME THING.

ARTUR WAS?
YUP. BUT I'M SURE HE'LL COME THROUGH. AS OUR NUMBER ONE PLAYER, HE KNOWS HE CAN'T TAKE THE DAY OFF.

WHOA! **WHOA!** ARTUR'S NOT THE ONLY ONE WHO CAN'T TAKE THE DAY OFF! **I** AM PERFECTLY CAPABLE OF BRINGING MY "A" GAME, **TOO!**

LET'S RUMBLE.
KNUTE ROCKNE'S GOT NOTHING ON ME.
Peirce

NATE WRIGHT OF P.S. 38 WILL PLAY ROGER MUNSON OF BISHOP RILEY.
I REMEMBER **YOU!** I BEAT YOU LAST YEAR IN THE STATE QUARTERFINALS!

YEAH, WELL... I HAPPENED TO BE GOING THROUGH A PERSONAL CRISIS THAT DAY.
OH, **REAL**LY! AND ARE YOU PLANNING ON "GOING THROUGH" SOMETHING TO**DAY**?

NOT SOME**THING**. SOME**ONE**.
Peirce

LET'S PLAY.

YOU KNOW HOW I CAN TELL I'M WINNING THIS MATCH, WRIGHT? YOU'RE SO **QUIET**! YOU'RE NOT DOING ANY OF YOUR TRADEMARK **WOOFING**!

CHECKMATE.
!

WOOF.
Peirce

SO, FOR A **CHANGE**, **ARTUR** WILL BE THE **HERO** AND EVERYONE WILL BE TALKING FOR **WEEKS** ABOUT HOW GREAT **ARTUR** IS!

I'M CONFLICTED. I DON'T KNOW WHETHER I WANT ARTUR TO WIN HIS MATCH OR NOT.
INVI
CH
TOUR

IF HE WINS, THEN WE WIN THE TOURNAMENT, AND THAT'S GOOD!...
BUT HE'LL ALSO GET ALL THE GLORY, WHICH IS BAD!

THEN AGAIN, I DO WANT US TO WIN!
... BUT I ALSO KIND OF WANT ARTUR TO LOSE!
BUT WHY CAN'T I JUST BE HAPPY FOR ARTUR'S SUCCESS?
BECAUSE! HASN'T HE HAD ENOUGH SUC-CESS?

BUT THAT'S SO SHALLOW!
SHALLOW, SHMALLOW! LET HIM GO DOWN!
IT'S LIKE BEING TEAM-MATES WITH GOLLUM.
Peirce

OOP.
OOP?
OOP WHAT?

ARTUR JUST MADE A MISTAKE. IT LOOKS LIKE HIS OPPONENT WILL...

YUP. CHECKMATE.
HE LOST.

Peirce

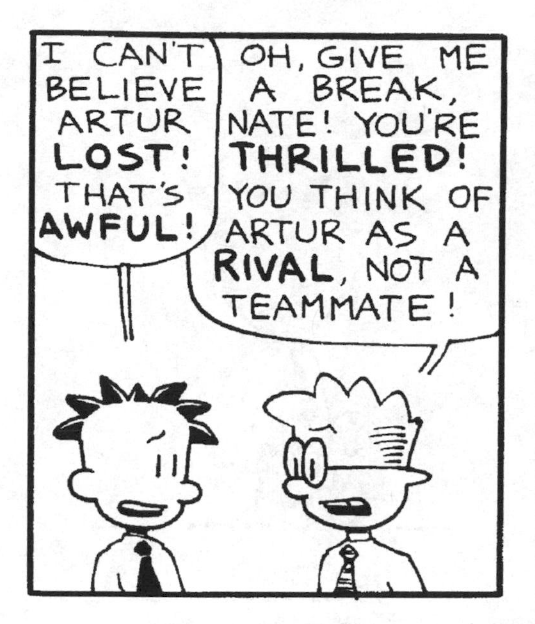
I CAN'T BELIEVE ARTUR **LOST**! THAT'S **AWFUL**!
OH, GIVE ME A BREAK, NATE! YOU'RE **THRILLED**! YOU THINK OF ARTUR AS A **RIVAL**, NOT A TEAMMATE!

WELL, YOU CAN STAY HERE AND GLOAT OVER HIS LOSS! **I'M** GONNA GO THANK HIM FOR DOING THE BEST HE COULD!

Peirce

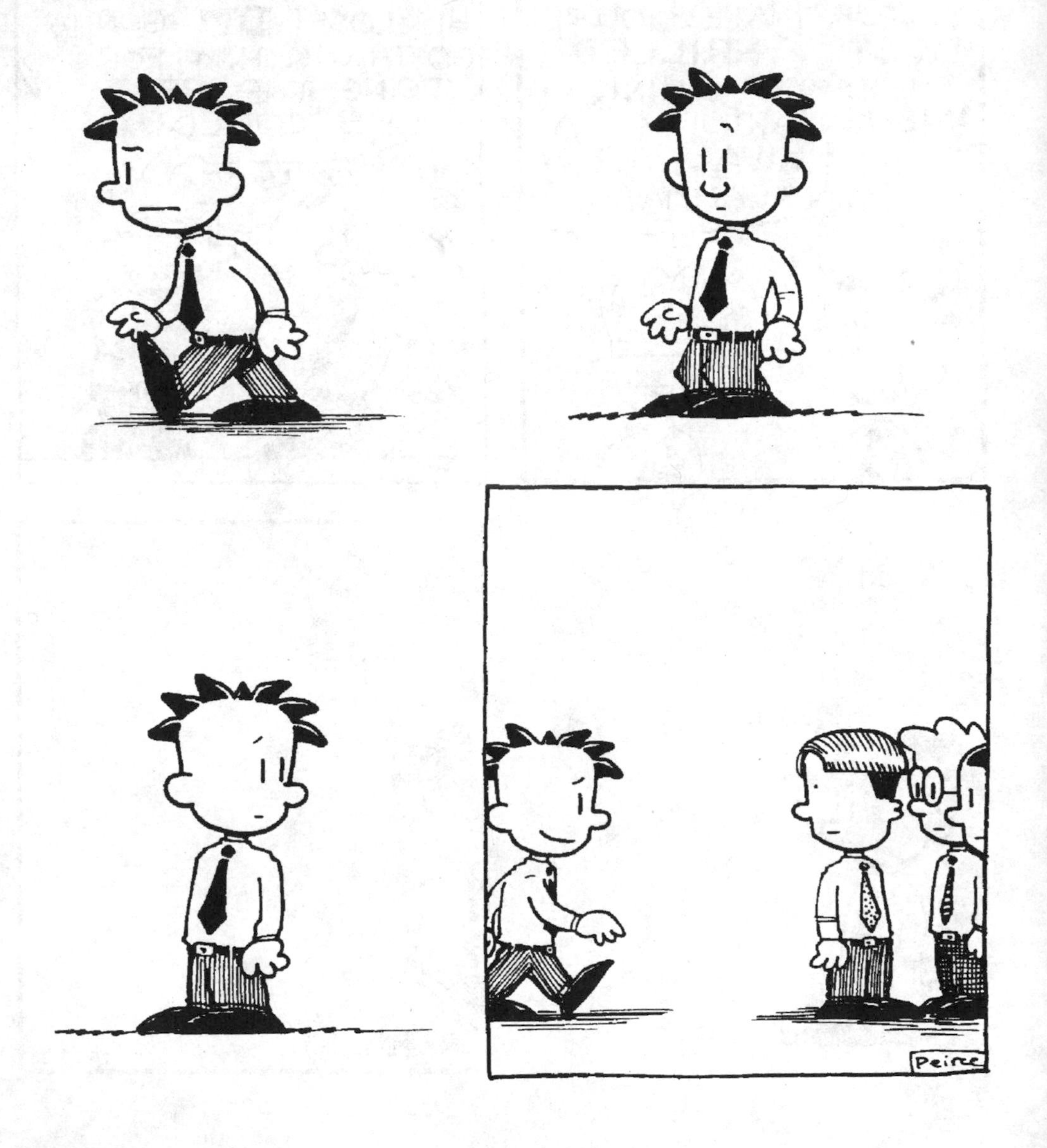
Peirce

UH... HEY, ARTUR.
HALLO, NATE.

NICE MATCH. YOU DESERVED TO WIN.
AH. IT IS NICE YOU ARE SAYING, BUT I DID NOT PLAY WELL.

YOU'LL HAVE OTHER CHANCES! THERE'LL BE OTHER TOURNA-MENTS!
THANK YOU, NATE. YOU ARE BEING VERY KIND TO ME.

WHY?
Peirce

I'VE GOT A LITTLE EXTRA MONEY, ARTUR! I'LL GET YOU A CANDY BAR!
I SEE WHAT YOU ARE DOING, NATE. YOU ARE TRYING TO MAKE ME FEEL BETTER.

YOU FEEL BAD FOR ME BECAUSE I LOST.
RIGHT!

WOULD YOU ALSO FEEL **HAPPY** FOR ME IF I HAD **WON**?

EAT YOUR "SNICKERS," ARTUR.
THANK YOU VERY MUCH.
Peirce

NATE? I'VE BEEN WATCHING. IT'S VERY KIND OF YOU TO TRY TO CONSOLE ARTUR.

IT'S PROBABLY NOT EASY FOR YOU. I REALIZE THAT YOU AND HE HAVE A BIT OF A RIVALRY.

...SO I JUST WANTED TO SAY THAT I APPRECIATE YOUR PUTTING YOUR PERSONAL FEELINGS ASIDE AND THINKING OF A TEAM-MATE FIRST!

HERE COMES THE SPELLING LESSON.
...BECAUSE THERE'S NO "I" IN **TEAM**!
Peirce

AMANDA WON "MOST POPULAR."
WHAT? OH, COME ON! SHE IS SO STUCK-UP!

GINA WON "BRAINIEST."
WHAT? SHE'S NOT BRAINY, SHE JUST SPENDS HER TIME MEMORIZING USELESS FACTS!

ANTHONY IS "MOST ATHLETIC."
WHAT? WHO DECIDED THAT? ANTHONY'S A SPAZ!

SHARON IS "CUTEST."
WHAT? HER FACE IS A TOTAL ZIT FARM!

...AND ZACK IS "FUNNIEST."
WHAT? OH, GIVE ME A BREAK! I'M MUCH FUNNIER THAN ZACK!

WHERE AM I ON THAT LIST? IF ALL THESE OTHER PEOPLE WON AWARDS, I MUST HAVE WON SOMETHING!

UMMMM... YUP, YOU'RE RIGHT HERE. YOU DID WIN SOMETHING.
WHAT? WHAT?

"BIGGEST ▬▬▬▬"
WHAT?

HOW COME YOU CIRCLED TODAY ON YOUR CALENDAR? THE LAST DAY OF SCHOOL ISN'T 'TIL **TOMORROW**!
HM? OH... UH...

I JUST MADE A MIS-TAKE, I GUESS. JUST A SIMPLE MISTAKE.

HE CIRCLED TODAY BECAUSE TODAY IS PRANK DAY.
WHA...? **PRANK** DAY?

WHAT IS THIS "PRANK DAY"?
I'LL BE CHECKING YOUR BACKPACK.
peirce

READY FOR PRANK DAY?
NO, UNFORTUNATELY! I GOT BUSTED!

MY DAD FOUND OUT ABOUT PRANK DAY AND PINCHED ALL MY STUFF! HE TOOK MY WHIPPED CREAM, MY EGGS, MY "SILLY STRING"....EVERYTHING!

BUT THAT'S OK! A GREAT MIND LIKE MINE CAN ALWAYS FIND WAYS TO IMPROVISE!
Peirce

DID HE JUST SAY "A GREAT MIND"?
GUYS, HELP ME CATCH THAT SQUIRREL!

HEY, SCHOOL, I BET YOU DON'T HAVE A CLUE WHAT'S IN STORE FOR YOU TODAY, DO YOU?
NATE...

DO THE WORDS "PRANK DAY" RING A BELL, PAL? YUP, YOU HEARD ME: PRANK DAY!
NATE!
PAT
PAT

YOU'RE GONNA GET "SCHOOLED"! GET IT? PREPARE TO BE PUNK'D, YOU PILE OF BRICKS!
NATE!

I'M TRYING TO GET HIM TO STOP TALKING TO THE WALL, BUT IT'S LIKE...
DON'T SAY IT.
YAK
YAK
YAK
Peirce

ALL RIGHT, PEOPLE, WE'RE GOING TO SPEND A FEW MINUTES ON GEOGRAPHY!

JUST LET ME PULL DOWN THE MAP AND...

Hi Mrs. Godfrey
Let's get jiggy

HA HA
A HA
HA HA
HA HA
HA HA
HA
I HATE PRANK DAY.
Peirce

ALL RIGHT, PEOPLE, ENOUGH OF THIS **PRANK DAY** NONSENSE! IT'S TIME TO...
CLOWN-GRAM!
MRS. GODFREY

CLOWN-GRAM FOR MRS. GODFREY! AH! **YOU** MUST BE MRS. GODFREY!

AHEM!... ME ME ME MEEEEE...
HA
HEH HEH
HA HA

SEEEEE YOOOOU... IN SEPTEMMMBERR...
HA HA HA HA
CRIPES.
HA HA HA HA
HA HA
Peirce

AH! PRINCIPAL NICHOLS! I SEE YOU SURVIVED PRANK DAY!
YES.

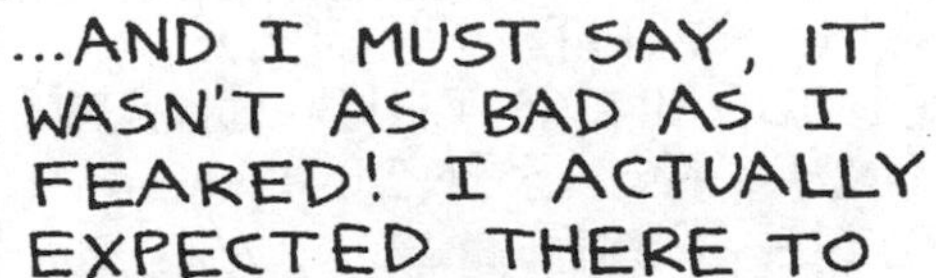
...AND I MUST SAY, IT WASN'T AS BAD AS I FEARED! I ACTUALLY EXPECTED THERE TO BE MORE...

EXIT

DUDE, WHERE'S MY CAR?
MMPH!
Peirce

LAST DAY OF SCHOOL! SO LONG, MRS. CZERWICKI!
SEE YOU NEXT FALL, NATE!

NEXT FALL? WELL...YEAH, I GUESS. I **HOPE** SO.
WHAT DO YOU MEAN?

WELL, NOTHING IS **CERTAIN**, AM I RIGHT? NEXT FALL IS STILL A LONG, **LONG** WAY OFF!

...AND A WOMAN OF YOUR AGE...
I'LL TRY TO HANG ON.
Peirce

GOING TO WORK AT THE ICE CREAM SHOP AGAIN THIS SUMMER, MR. ROSA?
NOT "WORKING AT THE ICE CREAM SHOP", NATE...

I'LL BE "MAKING ALL YOUR SWEET DREAMS COME TRUE"!

WA HA HA HA
HA HA HA HA
HA HA HA

WAIT... WHY AM I LAUGHING?
MAN, WHAT A LAME SLOGAN!
Peirce

PRINCIPAL NICHOLS! READY FOR THE SUMMER?
I CERTAINLY AM!

I CAN'T WAIT TO CLIMB INTO MY BATHING SUIT AND HIT THE BEACH!

WHOA! LOOK OUT, BEACH!
PAT PAT

THERE'S A GUY WHO NEEDS A VACATION.
Peirce

CLEANING OUT YOUR LOCKER, NATE?
YUP!

THIS IS A WHOLE YEAR'S WORTH OF WORK! ONE FULL YEAR OF ACADEMIC ACHIEVEMENT!
VERY IMPRES-SIVE!

WHUMP!
TRASH

SIGH...
MAN, THAT FELT GOOD!
Peirce

COUNTDOWN
TIK
TIK
TIK
TIK
TIK
TIK

IGNITION
RRRINNG!!

LIFT-OFF
ZOW!

ESCAPE VELOCITY
peirce

PENCIL...

...PAPER!

DONE!

DONE WITH WHAT?

Nate's
"TO DO" LIST

BUT YOU DIDN'T WRITE ANY–...

AHHHHH, SUMMER!
Peirce